Contents

*C = copper; B = bronze; ( ) = the line must be played but cannot be assessed for a Medal.

The King's Procession

Kit Turnbull

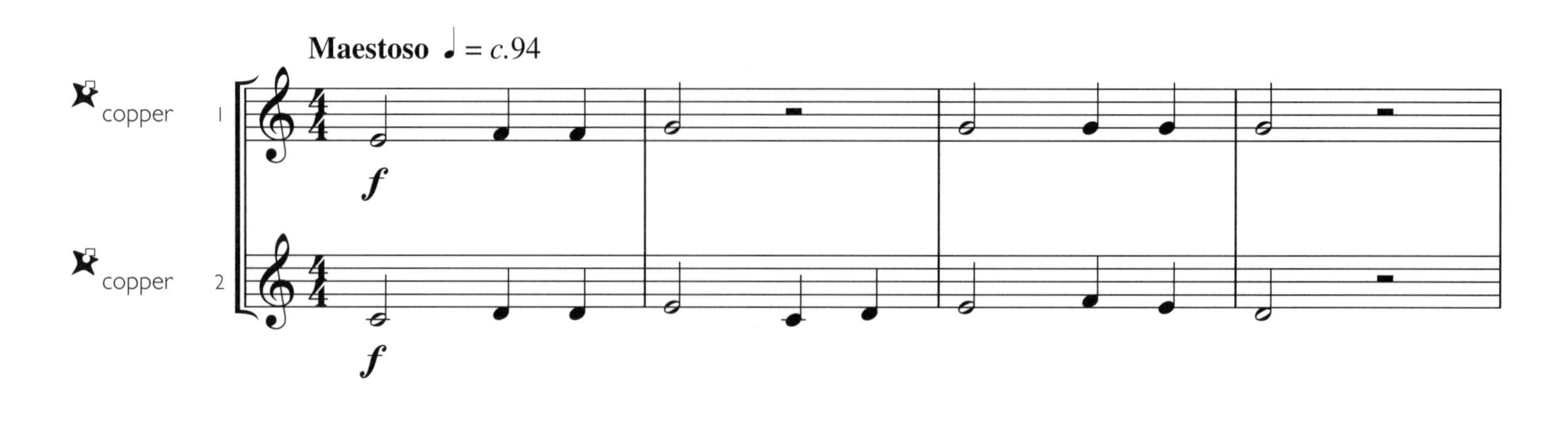

© 2004 by The Associated Board of the Royal Schools of Music

Bluebells

Nick Breeze

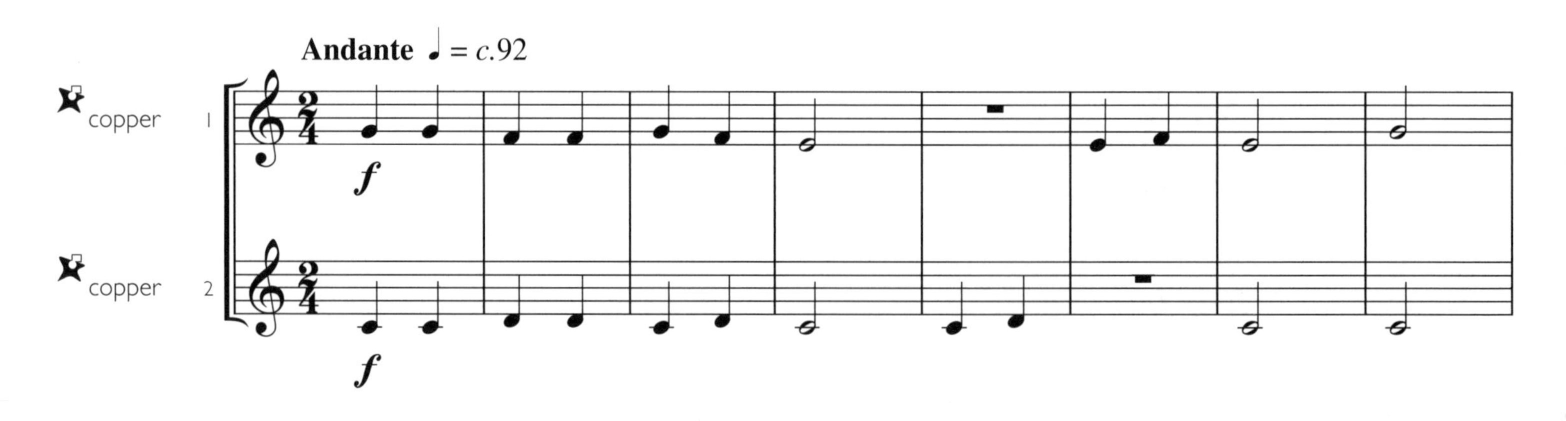

© 2004 by The Associated Board of the Royal Schools of Music

March of the Mouthpiece

Paul Harris

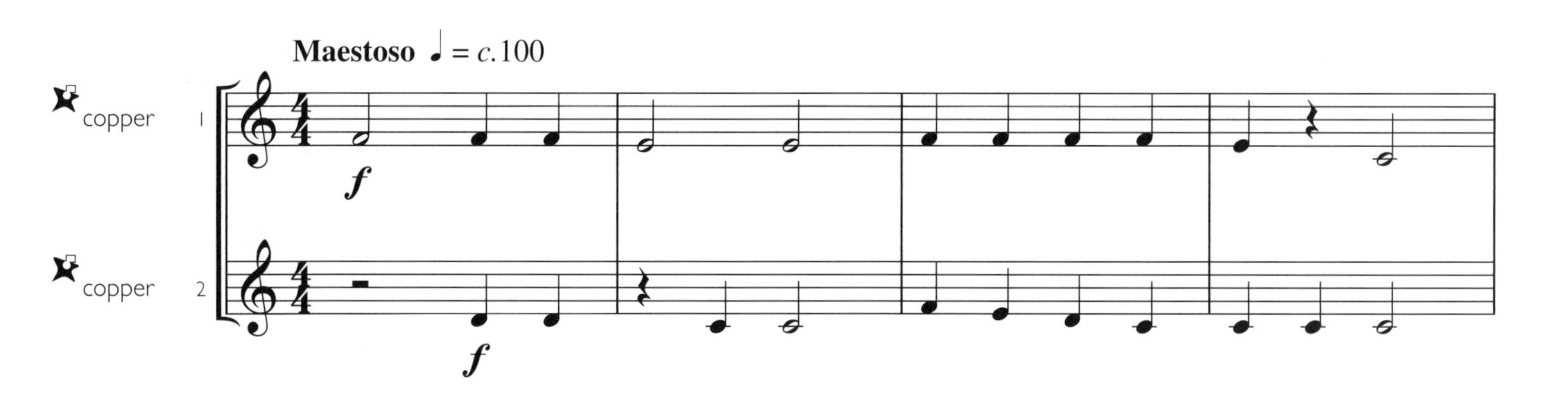

© 2004 by The Associated Board of the Royal Schools of Music

Leap-Frog

Nick Breeze

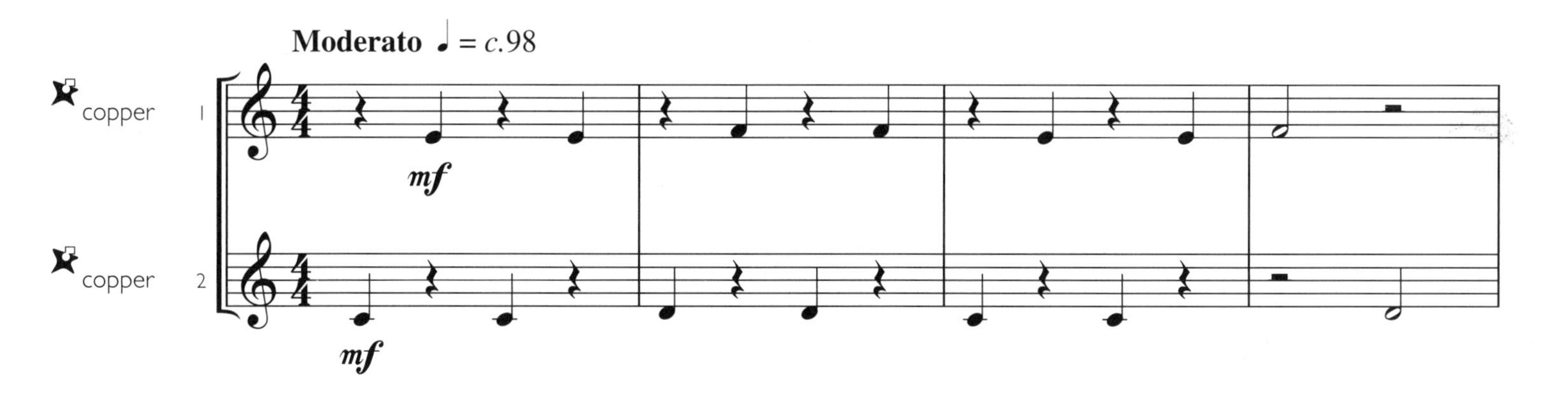

© 2004 by The Associated Board of the Royal Schools of Music

Heavy Metal Brass

Chris Batchelor

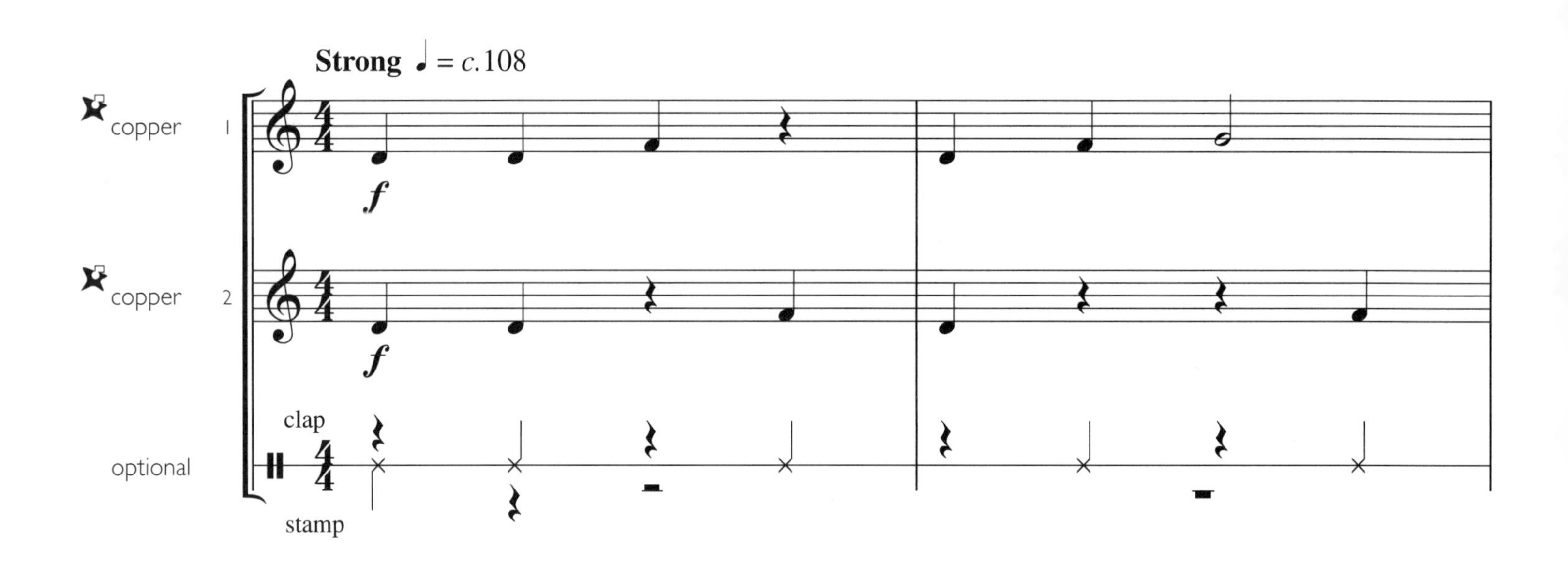

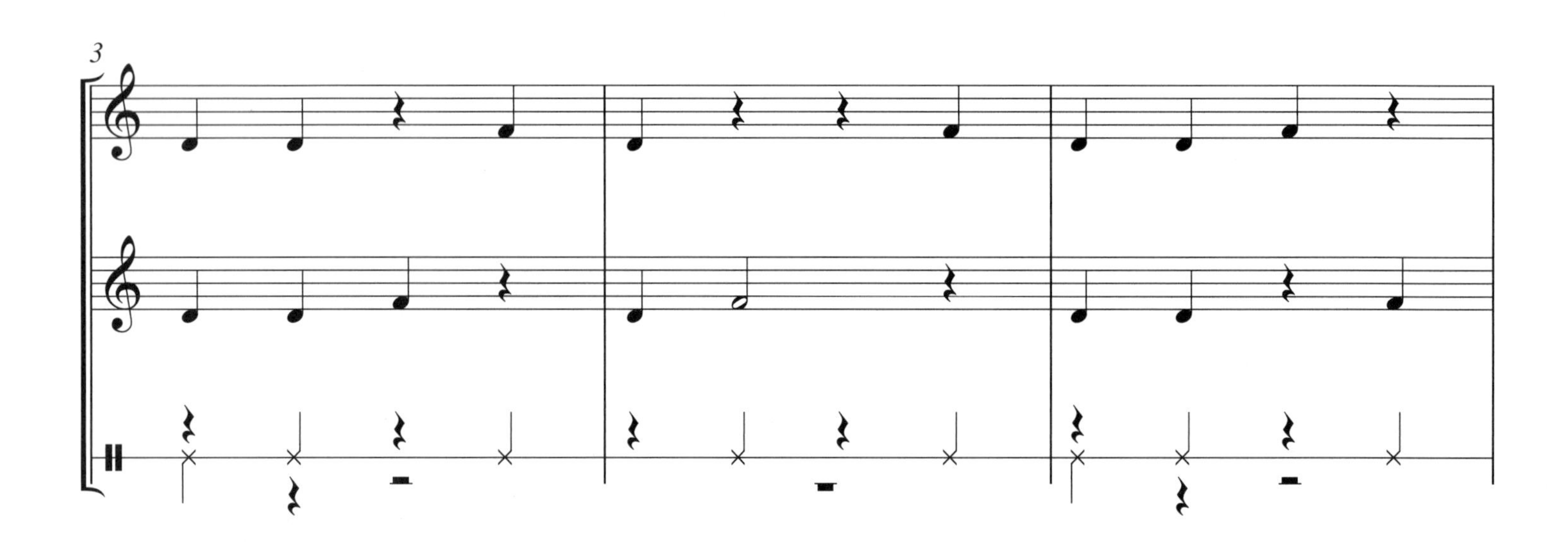

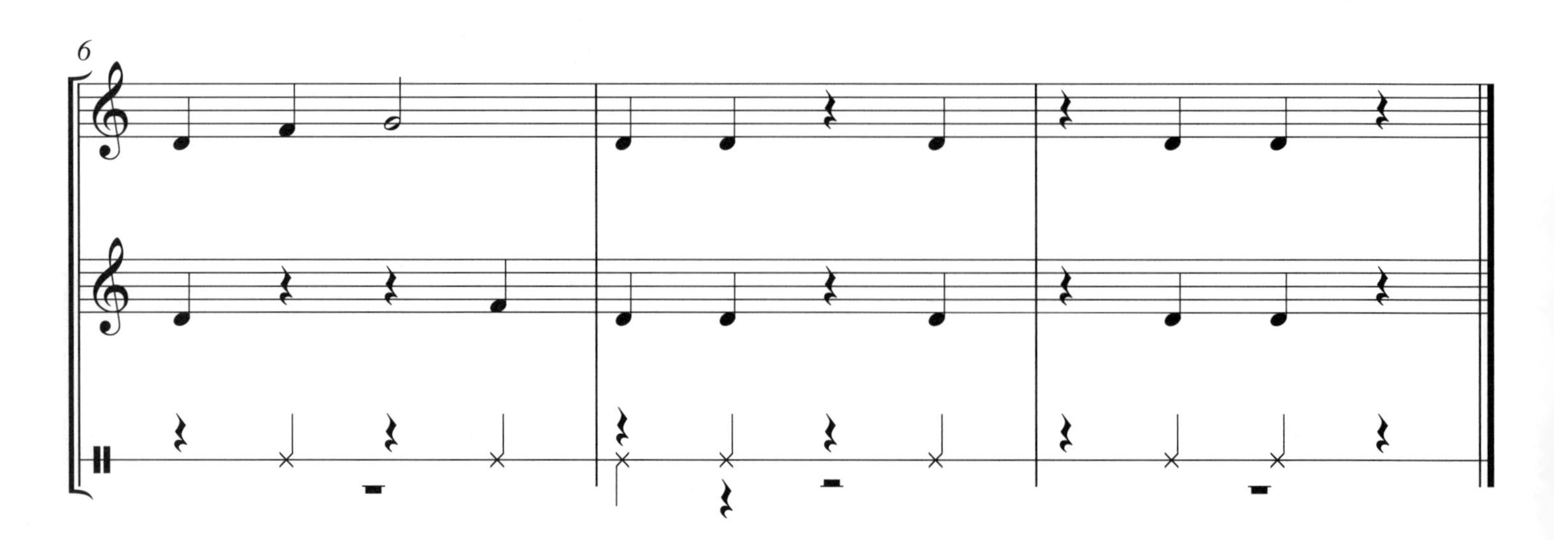

© 2004 by The Associated Board of the Royal Schools of Music

Traffic Jam

Robert Tucker

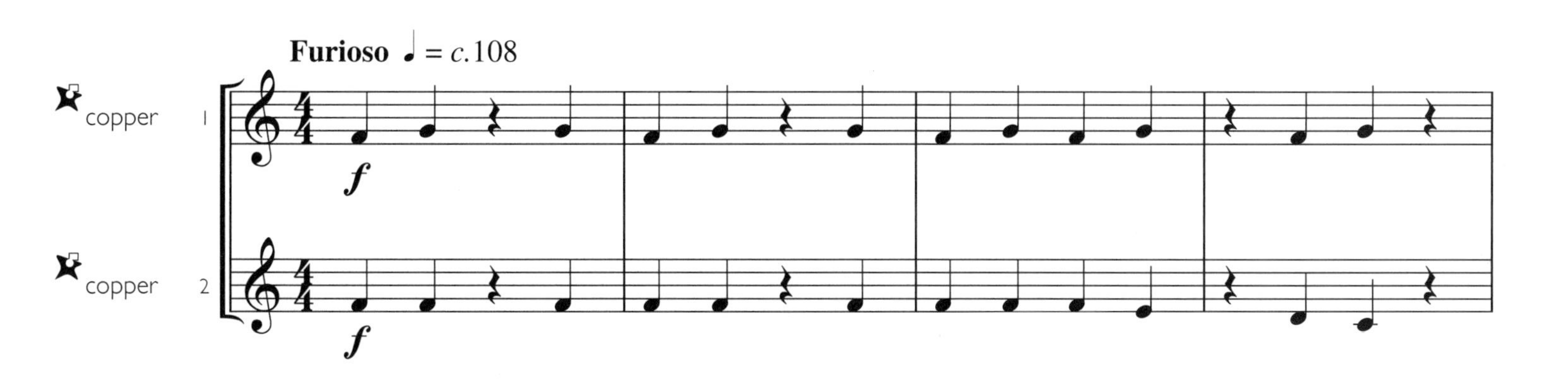

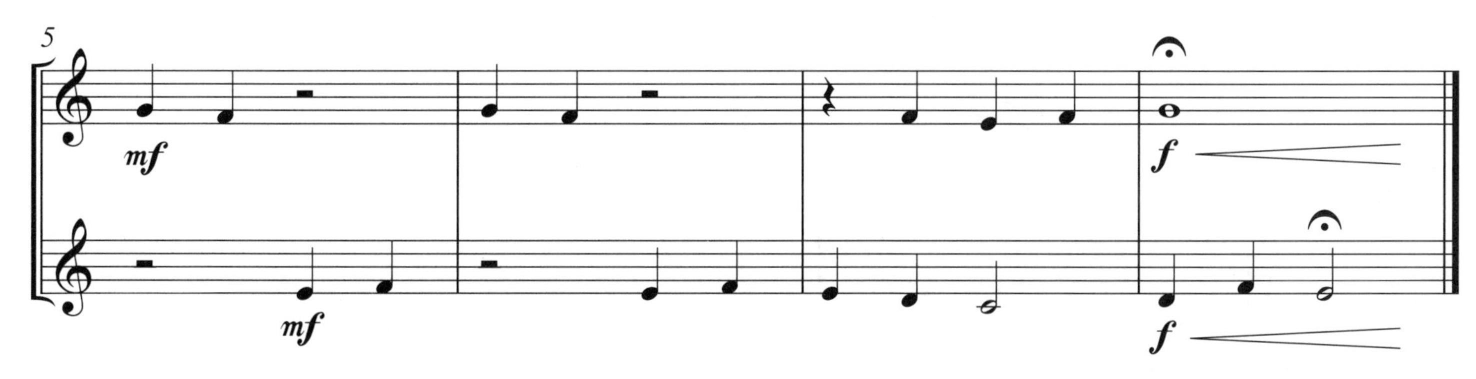

© 2004 by The Associated Board of the Royal Schools of Music

To Me – To You!

Stephen Roberts

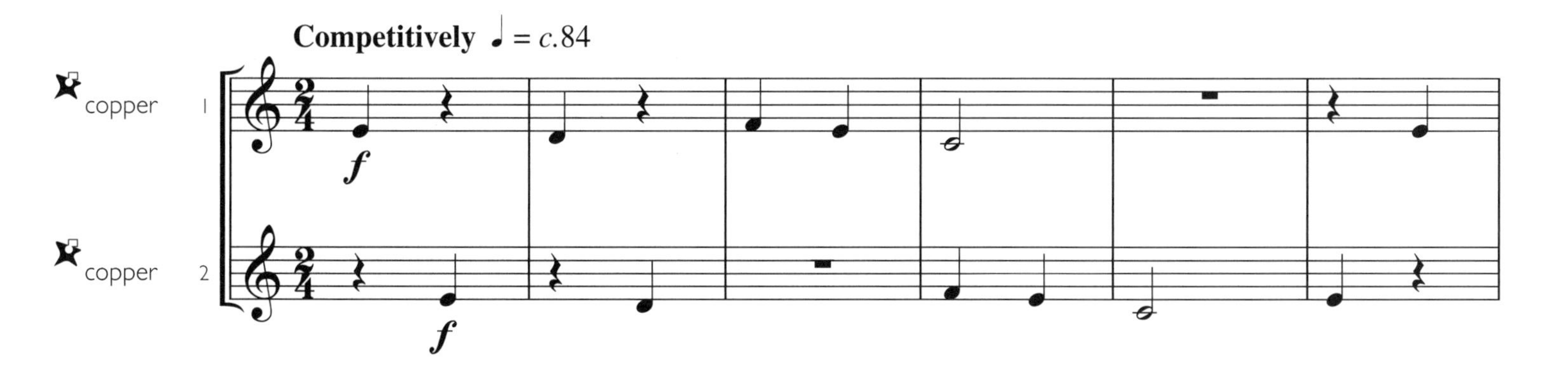

© 2004 by The Associated Board of the Royal Schools of Music

Step by Step

Kit Turnbull

© 2004 by The Associated Board of the Royal Schools of Music

Star-Gazing

Stephen Roberts

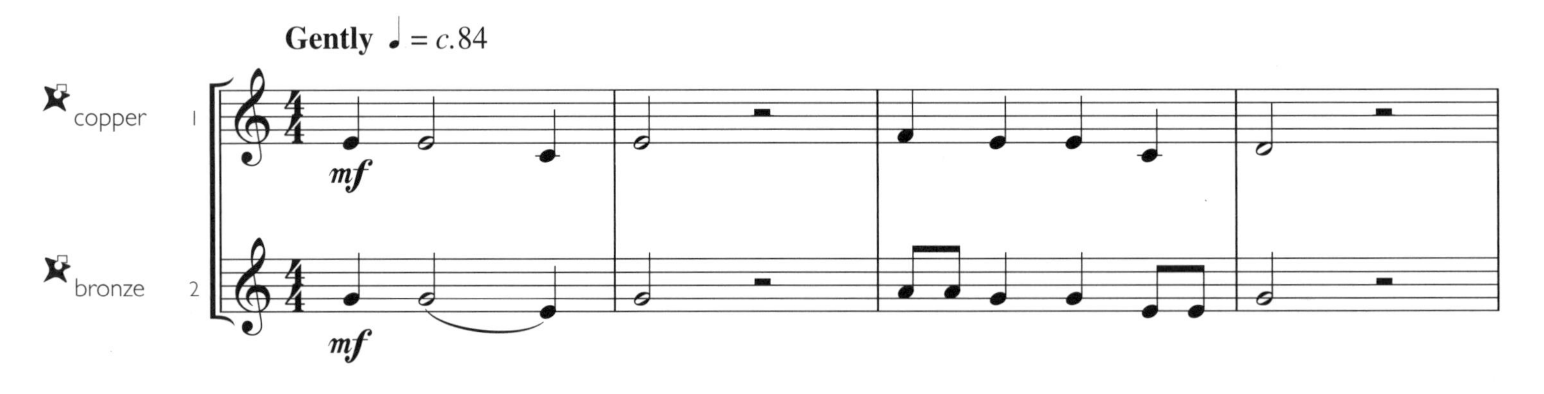

© 2004 by The Associated Board of the Royal Schools of Music

Funky Riff

Chris Batchelor

© 2004 by The Associated Board of the Royal Schools of Music

The Mole

Henry Bowers-Broadbent

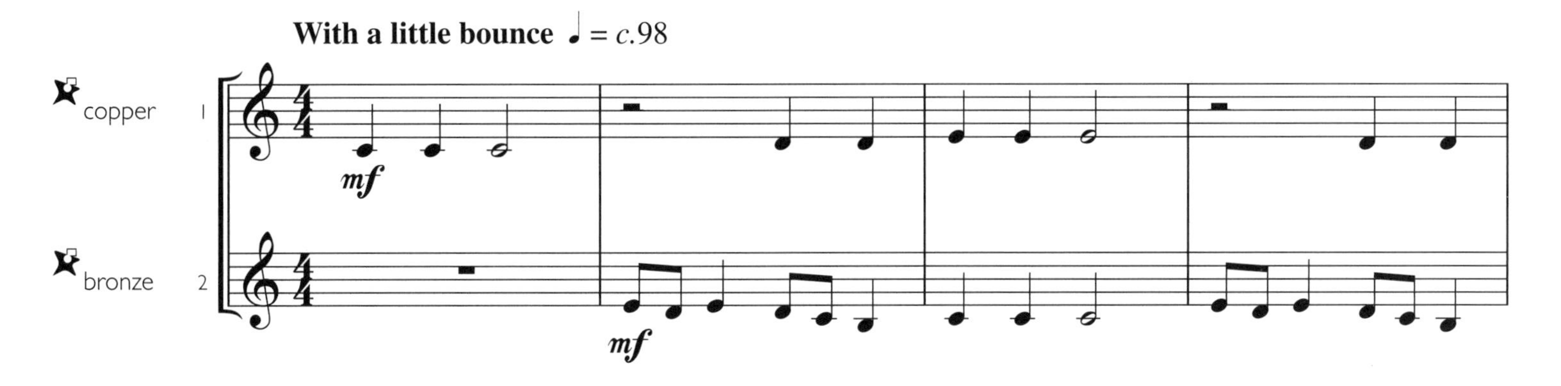

© 2004 by The Associated Board of the Royal Schools of Music

Passing Clouds

Nick Breeze

© 2004 by The Associated Board of the Royal Schools of Music

Another Tea-Cake, Your Majesty?

Andrew Tyrrell

© 2004 by The Associated Board of the Royal Schools of Music

Blue Haze

Nick Breeze

© 2004 by The Associated Board of the Royal Schools of Music

Beans on Toast

Nigel Scaife

© 2004 by The Associated Board of the Royal Schools of Music

First Things First

Paul Archibald

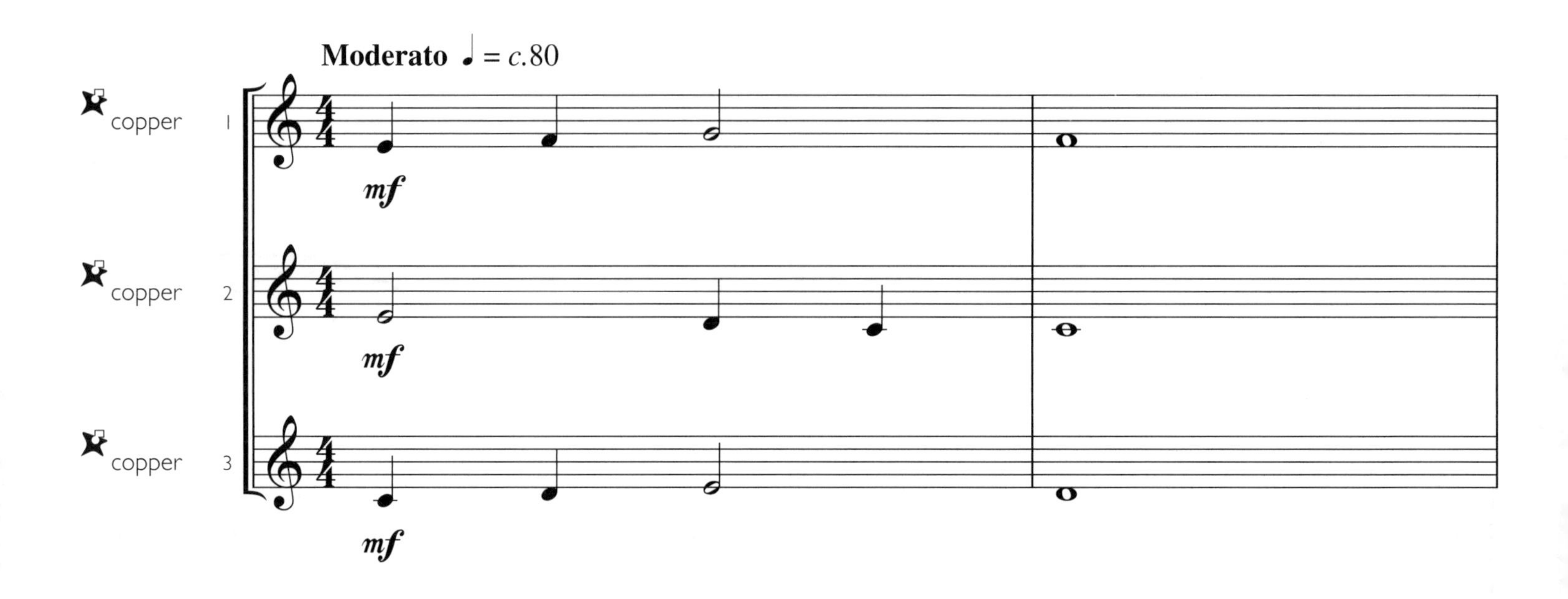

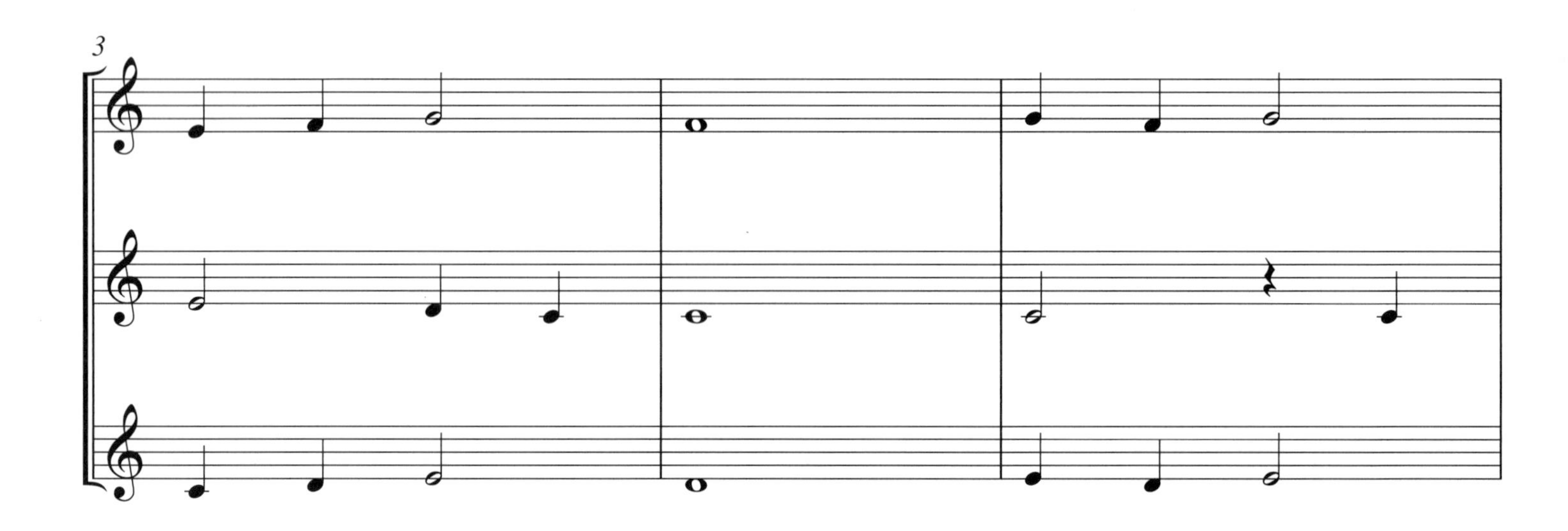

© 2004 by The Associated Board of the Royal Schools of Music

To and Fro

Henry Bowers-Broadbent

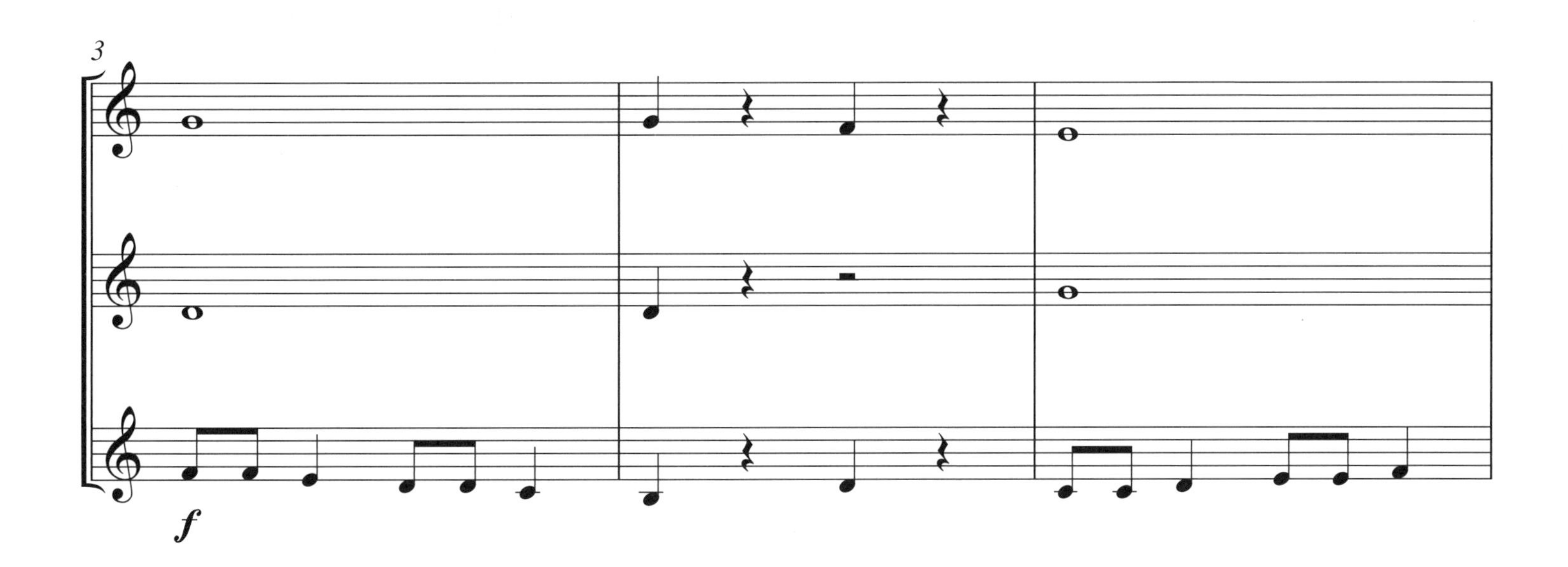

© 2004 by The Associated Board of the Royal Schools of Music

Pavane for a Sick Elephant

Andrew Tyrrell

© 2004 by The Associated Board of the Royal Schools of Music

Blue in the Face

Henry Bowers-Broadbent

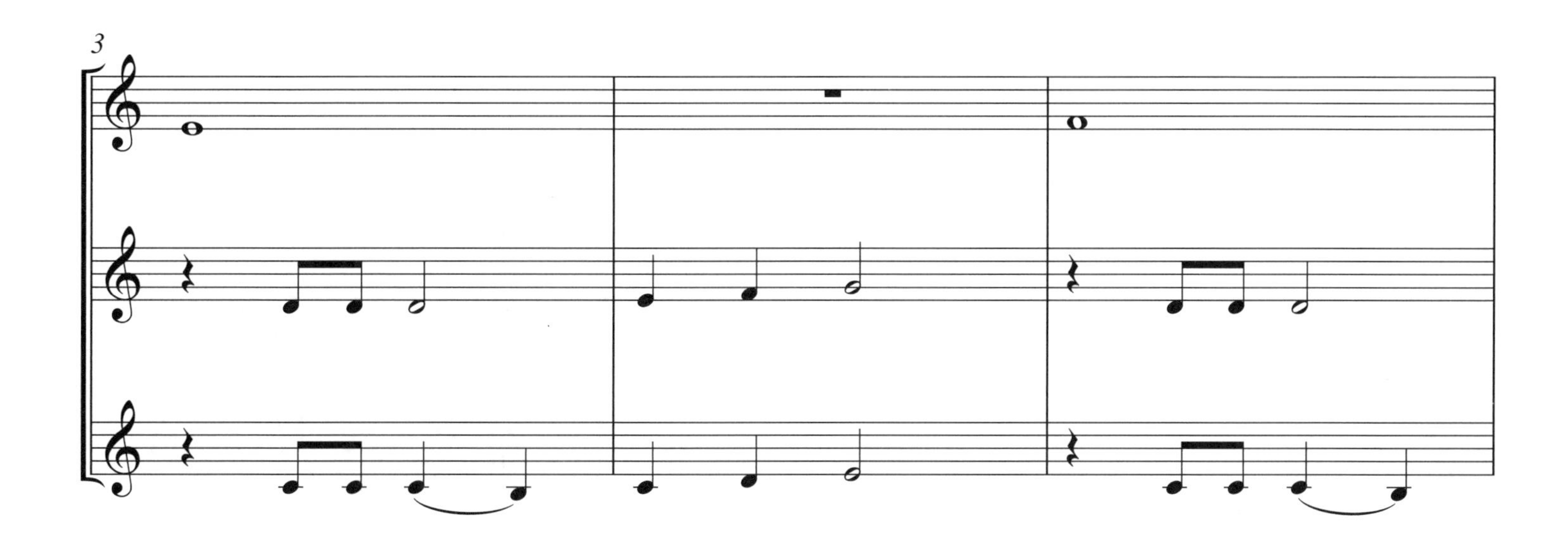

© 2004 by The Associated Board of the Royal Schools of Music

C-Breeze

Nigel Scaife

© 2004 by The Associated Board of the Royal Schools of Music

Duck Chase

Op. 176a

Derek Bourgeois

© 2004 by The Associated Board of the Royal Schools of Music

Jingle Bells

J. Pierpoint arr. John Miller

© 2004 by The Associated Board of the Royal Schools of Music 4/08

50 FILM TUNES FOR CLARINET
GRADED

Published by
Wise Publications
14-15 Berners Street, London W1T 3LJ, UK.

Exclusive Distributors:
Music Sales Limited
Distribution Centre, Newmarket Road,
Bury St Edmunds, Suffolk IP33 3YB, UK.
Music Sales Corporation
257 Park Avenue South, New York, NY 10010, USA.
Music Sales Pty Limited
20 Resolution Drive, Caringbah, NSW 2229, Australia.

Order No. AM997898
ISBN 978-1-84938-136-9
This book © Copyright 2009 Wise Publications,
a division of Music Sales Limited.

Unauthorised reproduction of any part of this publication by
any means including photocopying is an infringement of copyright.

Edited by Jenni Wheeler.
Music processed by Camden Music.
Printed in the EU.

Your Guarantee of Quality
As publishers, we strive to produce every book to
the highest commercial standards.
This book has been carefully designed to minimise awkward
page turns and to make playing from it a real pleasure.
Particular care has been given to specifying acid-free, neutral-sized
paper made from pulps which have not been elemental chlorine bleached.
This pulp is from farmed sustainable forests and
was produced with special regard for the environment.
Throughout, the printing and binding have been planned to ensure
a sturdy, attractive publication which should give years of enjoyment.
If your copy fails to meet our high standards,
please inform us and we will gladly replace it.

www.musicsales.com

WISE PUBLICATIONS
part of The Music Sales Group

London / New York / Paris / Sydney / Copenhagen / Berlin / Madrid / Tokyo

GRADING NOTES

The pieces in this book have been carefully graded according to
various criteria such as rhythmic complexity, phrasing, tempo, key, range, etc.
Look for the number of stars for each piece to give you
an idea of the approximate playing level.
All musicians have particular strengths and weaknesses,
so the grading offered here should be taken as a suggestion only.

Generally, pieces with one star have simple rhythms,
straight forward phrasings and few difficult intervals;
essentially diatonic and in easier keys.

Pieces with two stars will have more challenging passages,
perhaps containing more rhythmic complexity,
more advanced key signatures and possibly explore a wider
range on the instrument.

Three-star pieces may include chromaticism,
challenging articulation and more advanced positioning.
Read through rhythms and keys before playing, and check for
time-signature changes and correct phrasing.

All Love Can Be
(from 'A Beautiful Mind')

Words by Will Jennings & Music by James Horner

© Copyright 2001 WillJennings Music Incorporated/Horner Music Incorporated/SKG Music Publishing LLC/Songs Of Universal Incorporated, USA/Universal Music Corporation, USA.
Universal Music Publishing Limited (75%)/Cherry Lane Music Limited (25%).
All rights in Germany administered by Universal Music Publ. GmbH.
All Rights Reserved. International Copyright Secured.

Baby Elephant Walk
(from 'Hatari!')

Music by Henry Mancini

© Copyright 1962 Famous Music LLC, USA.
All Rights Reserved. International Copyright Secured.

Back To The Future (Theme)

(from 'Back To The Future')

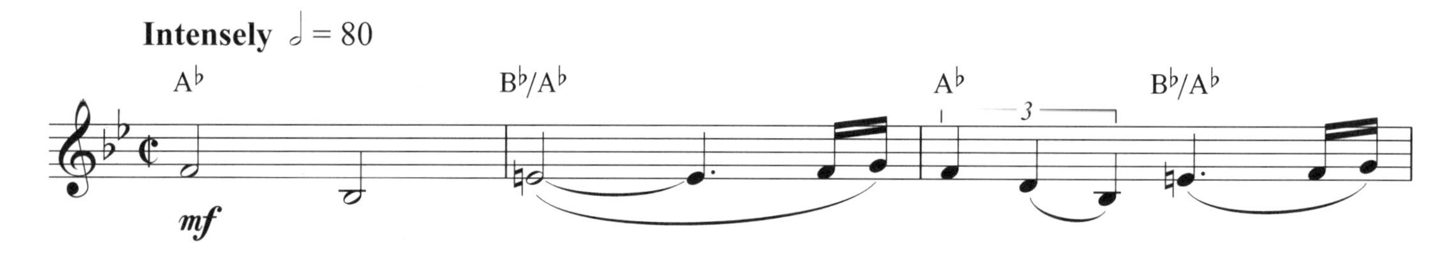

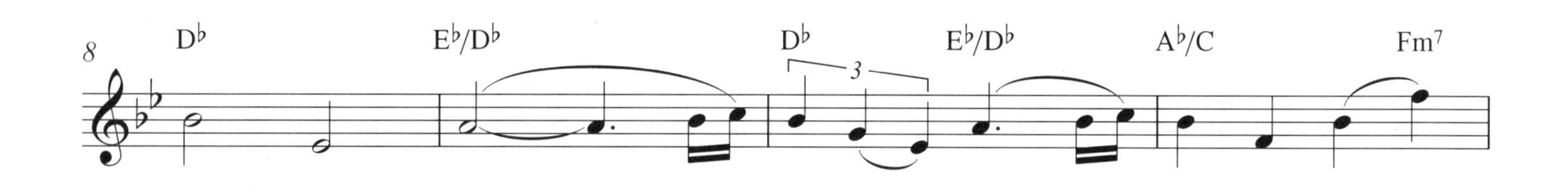

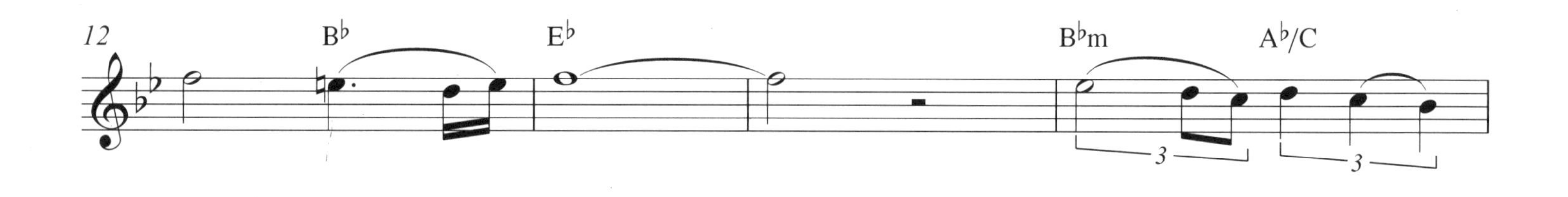

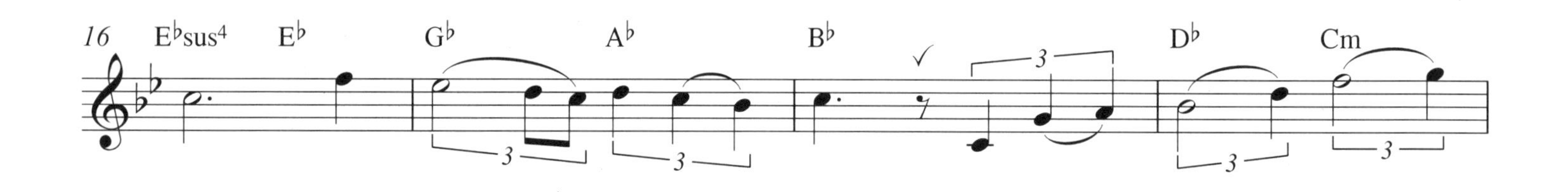

© Copyright 1985 MCA Music (a division of MCA Incorporated), USA. Universal/MCA Music Limited.
All rights in Germany administered by Universal/MCA Music Publ. GmbH.
All Rights Reserved. International Copyright Secured.

25
E♭
F/E♭
E♭
F/E♭

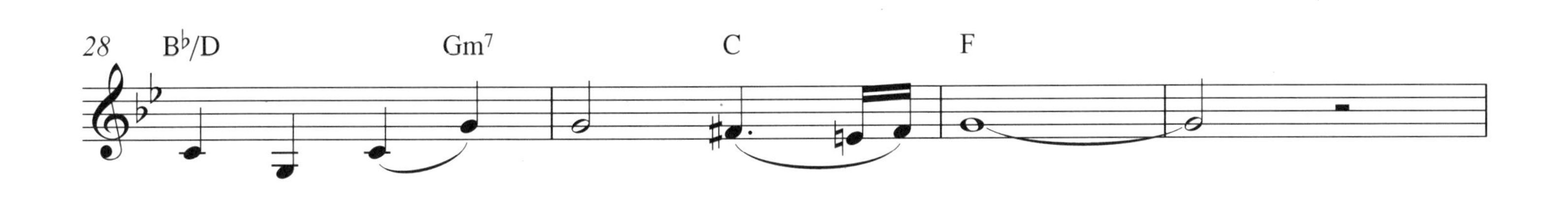
28
B♭/D
Gm7
C
F

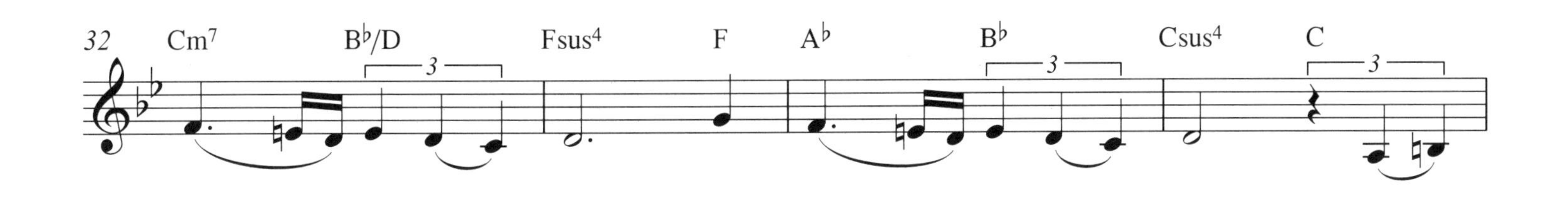
32
Cm7
B♭/D
Fsus4
F
A♭
B♭
Csus4
C

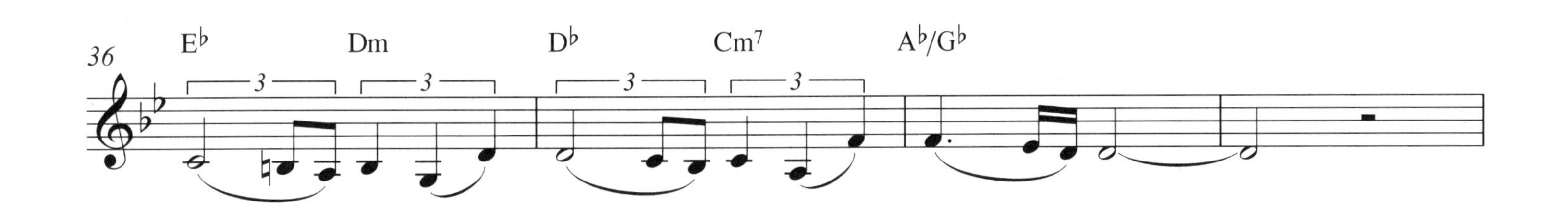
36
E♭
Dm
D♭
Cm7
A♭/G♭

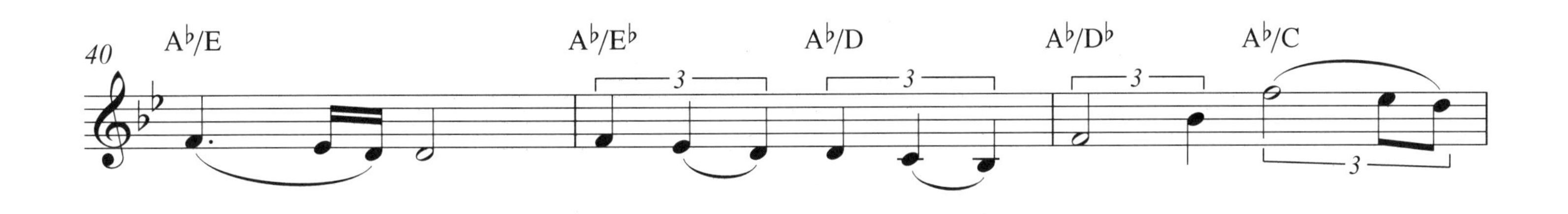
40
A♭/E
A♭/E♭
A♭/D
A♭/D♭
A♭/C

43
B♭m
D♭/E♭
E♭
A♭
ff

Betty et Zorg
(from 'Betty Blue')

Music by Gabriel Yared

© Copyright 1985 DE BOP. Assigned to CARGO FILMS.
Administered for the world by Premiere Music Group SARL.
All Rights Reserved. International Copyright Secured.

Build Me Up Buttercup
(from 'There's Something About Mary')

Words & Music by Michael D'Abo & Tony Macaulay

© Copyright 1968 EMI United Partnership Limited (75%)/Universal Music Publishing MGB Limited (18.75%)/Sony/ATV Music Publishing (UK) Limited (6.25%).
All Rights in Germany Administered by Musik Edition Discoton GmbH (A Division of Universal Music Publishing Group).
All Rights Reserved. International Copyright Secured.

Blue Velvet
(from 'Blue Velvet')

Words & Music by Bernie Wayne & Lee Morris

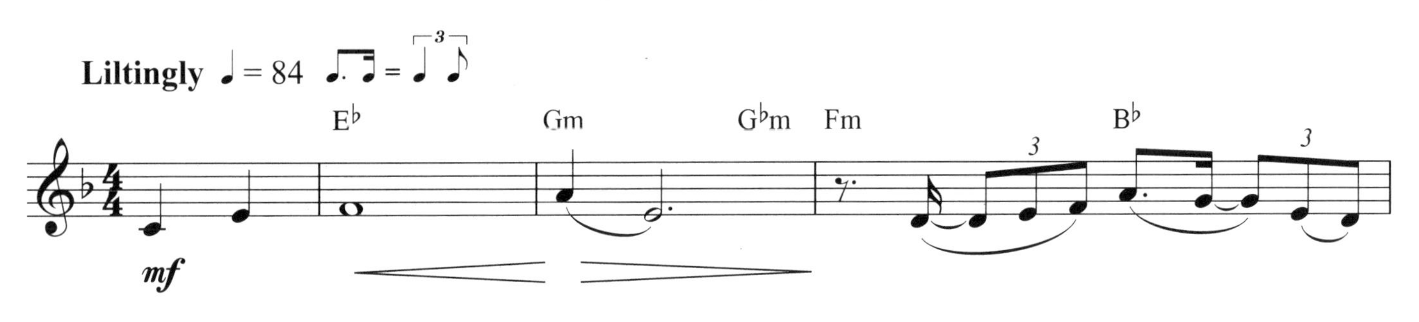

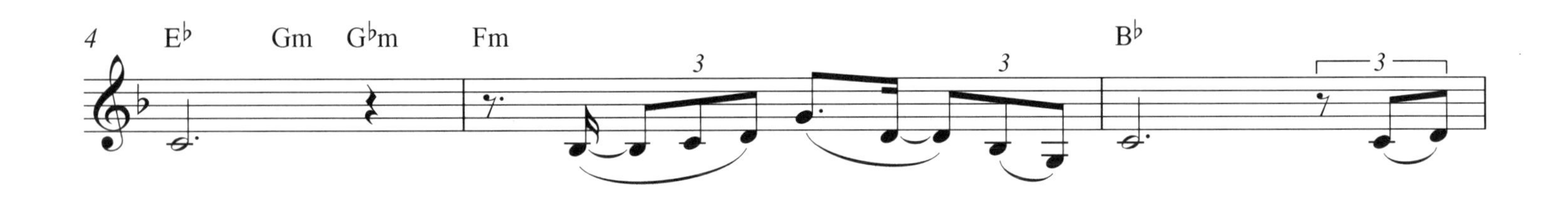

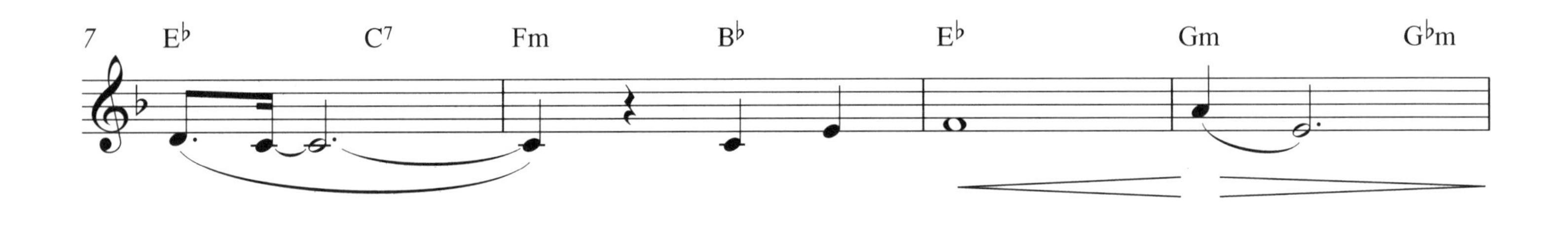

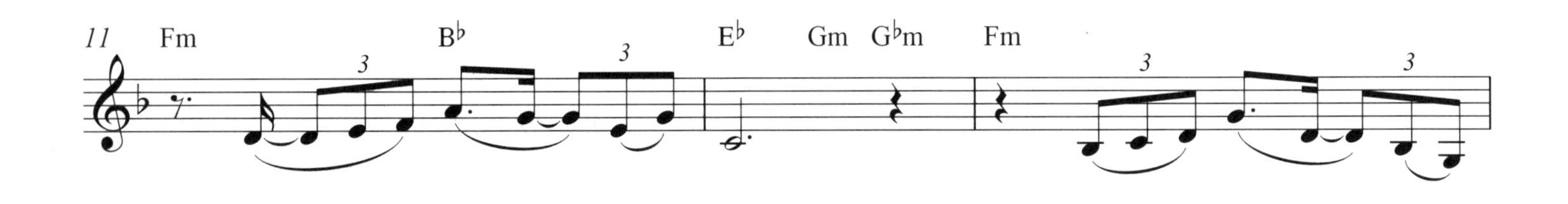

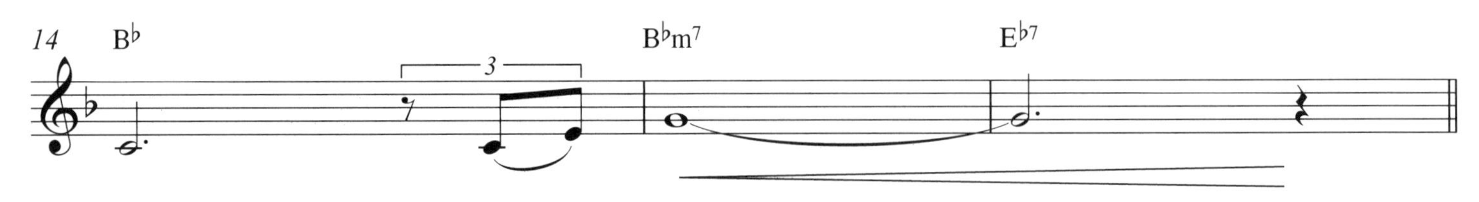

© Copyright 1951 Meridian Music Corporation/Vogue Music Incorporated, USA.
Chappell Morris Limited (50%)/I Q Music Limited (50%).
All Rights Reserved. International Copyright Secured.

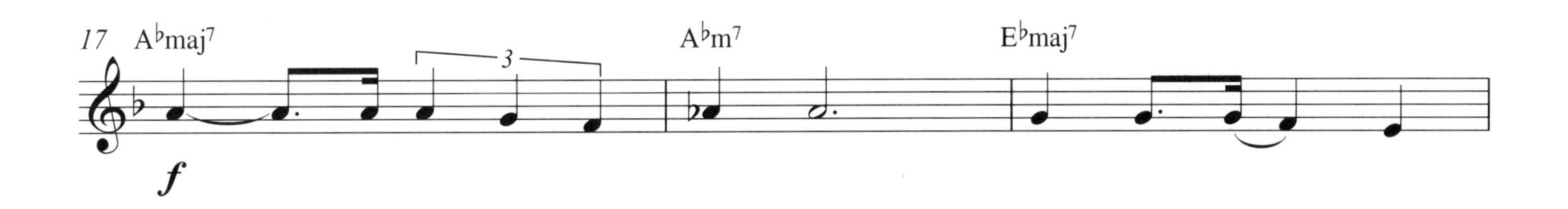
17 A♭maj7
3
A♭m7
E♭maj7
f

20 E♭7
A♭maj7
3
A♭m7
Gm
3
G♭m6

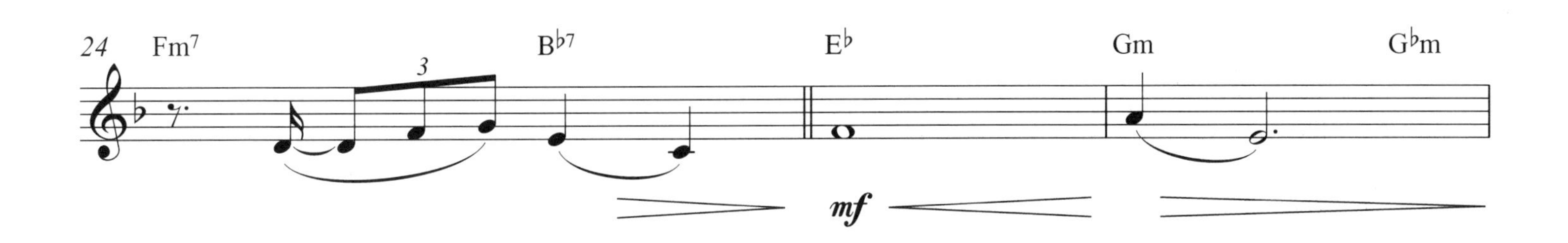
24 Fm7
3
B♭7
E♭
Gm
G♭m
mf

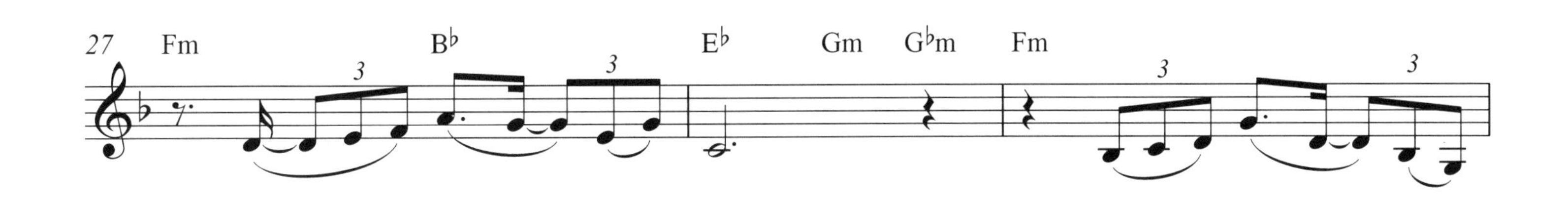
27 Fm
3
B♭
3
E♭
Gm
G♭m
Fm
3
3

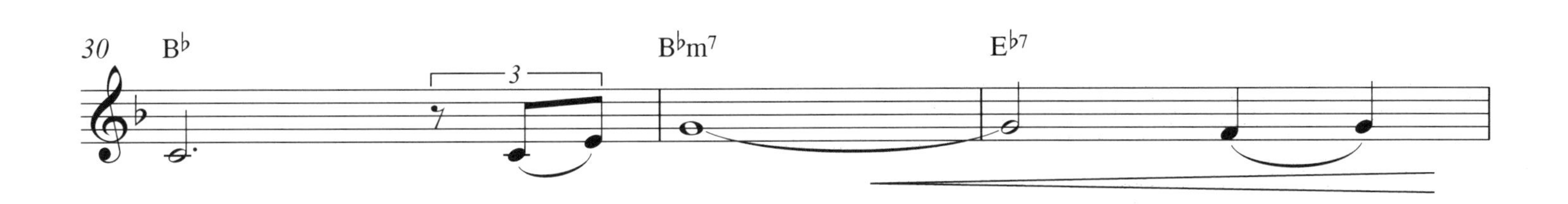
30 B♭
3
B♭m7
E♭7

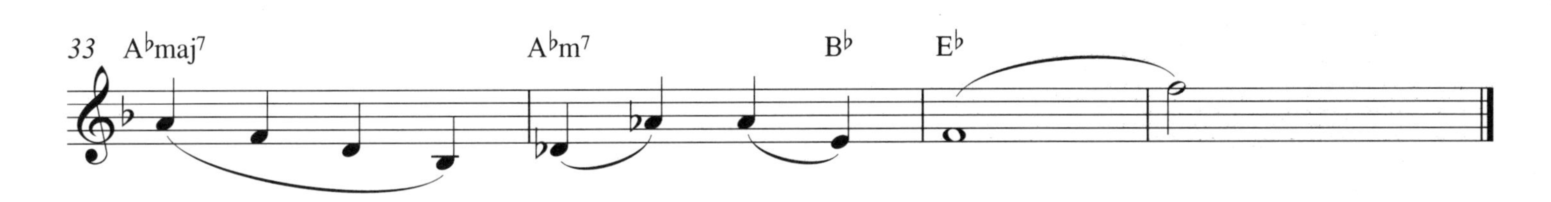
33 A♭maj7
A♭m7
B♭
E♭

Circle Of Life
(from Walt Disney Pictures' 'The Lion King')

Words by Tim Rice & Music by Elton John

© Copyright 1994 Wonderland Music Company Incorporated, USA.
All Rights Reserved. International Copyright Secured.

Clair De Lune
(from 'Ocean's 11')

Music by Claude Debussy

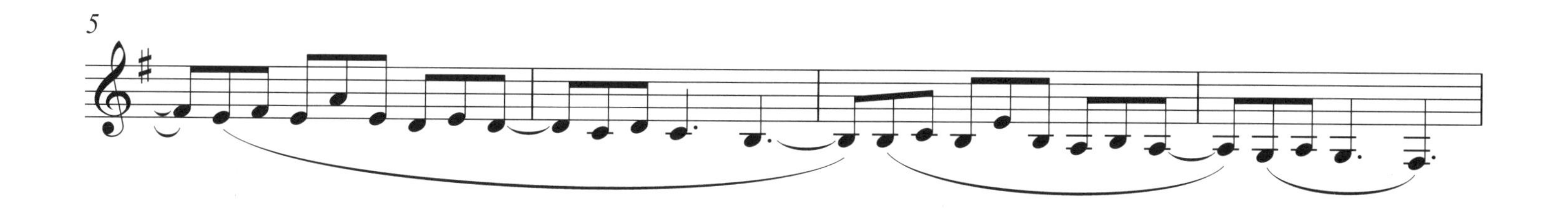

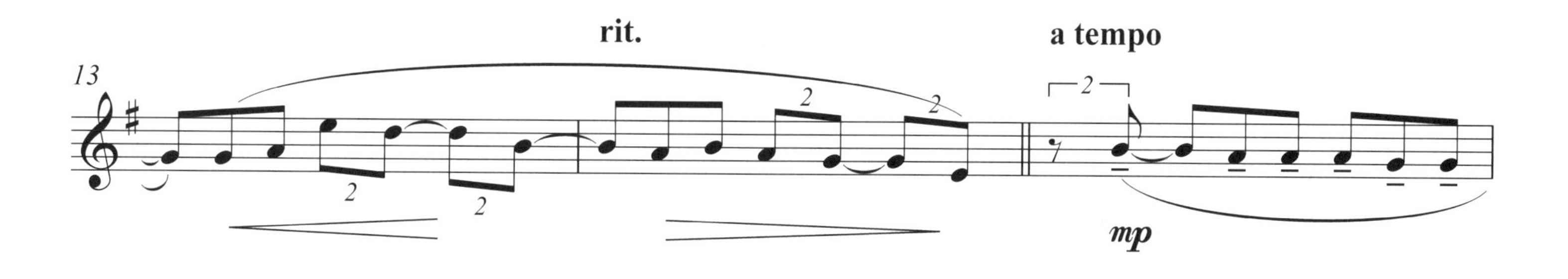

a tempo, gradually building

© Copyright 2009 Dorsey Brothers Music Limited.
All Rights Reserved. International Copyright Secured.

poco rit.

23

27
with more movement

31
pushing forward

36

41
more calmly
molto dim.

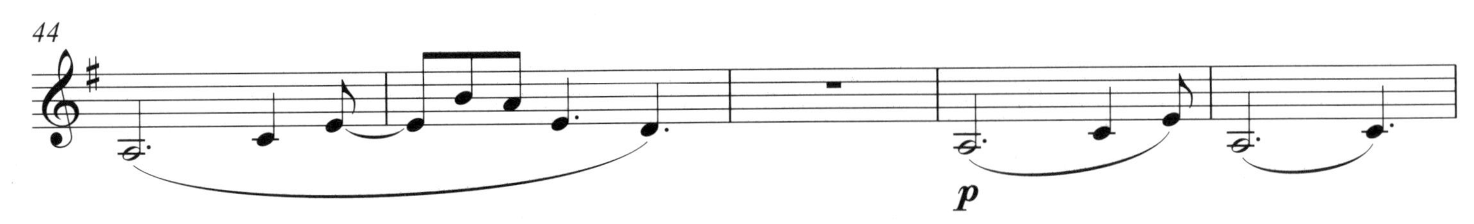
44

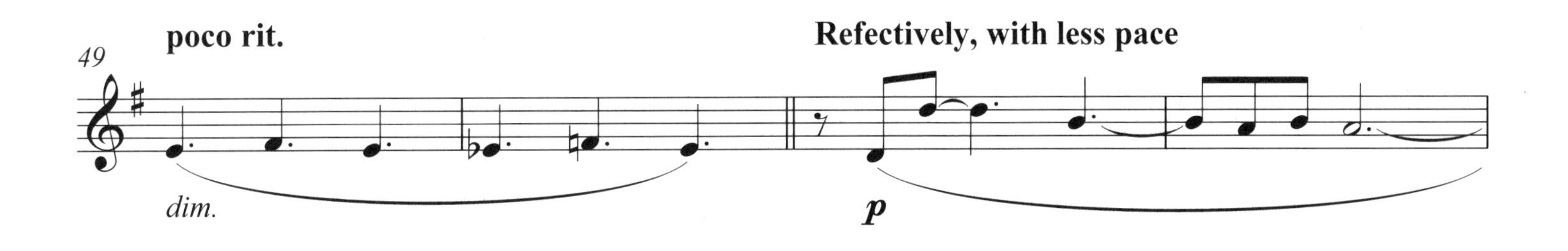
49
poco rit.
Refectively, with less pace
dim.
p

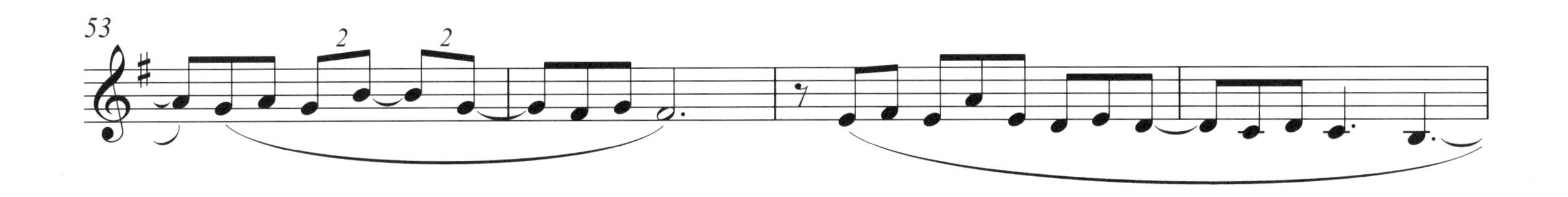
53
2
2

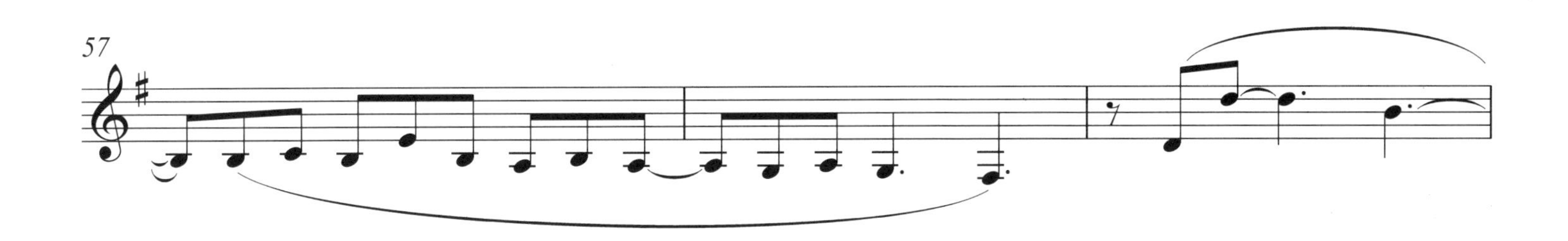
57

60

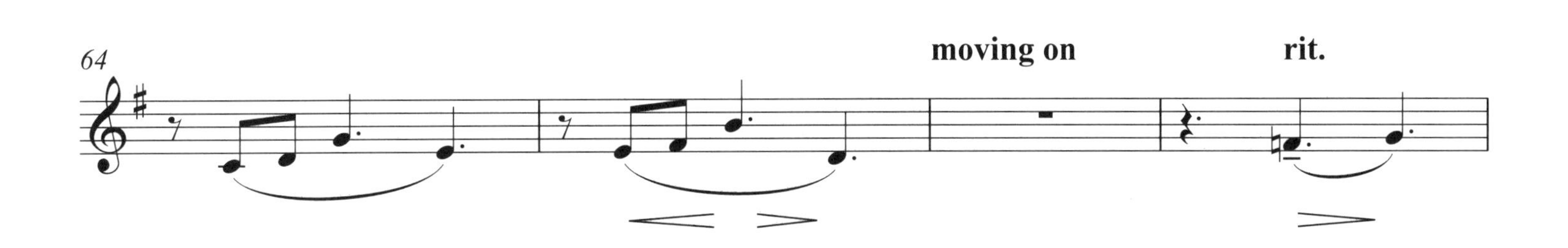
64
moving on
rit.

68
moving on
rit. al fine

Come What May
(from 'Moulin Rouge')

Words & Music by David Baerwald

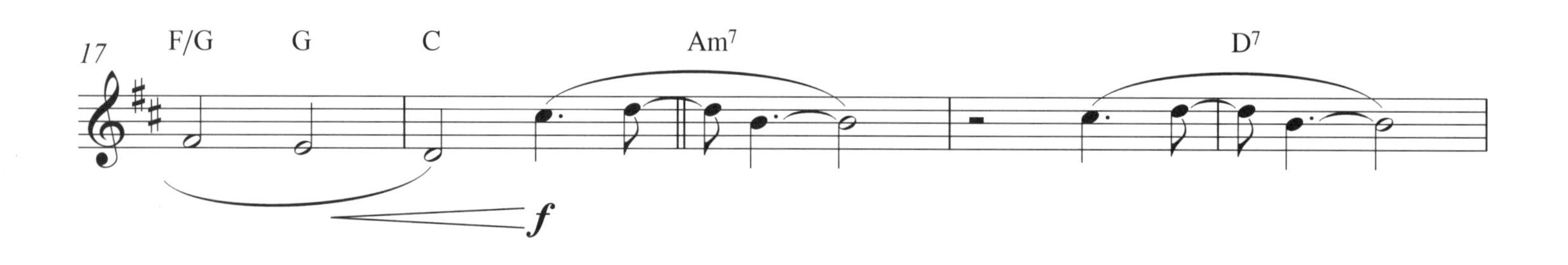

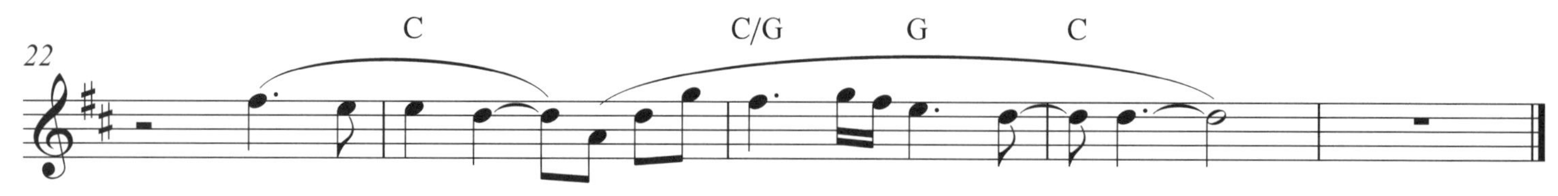

© Copyright 2001 TCF Music Publishing Incorporated (25%)/Almo Music Corporation/Zen Of Iniquity, USA.
Universal Music Publishing Limited (75%) (administered in Germany by Universal Music Publ. GmbH).
All Rights Reserved. International Copyright Secured.

GoldenEye
(from 'GoldenEye')

Words & Music by Bono & The Edge

© Copyright 1995 Blue Mountain Music Limited/Mother Music/PolyGram International Music Publishing Limited.
All Rights Reserved. International Copyright Secured.

21
Fm
Cm/E♭
Dm7(♭5)
24
mp
Cm
Dm
27 Cm/E♭
Fm
Cm
Dm
cresc. poco a poco
31 Cm/E♭
Gm
f
35
Gm
E♭/G
Gm6
E♭/G
mp misterioso
39
Gm
E♭/G
F
42
D
Gm
E♭/G
Gm6
46
E♭/G
Gm
E♭/G
49
F
D
Fm
f espressivo

52 Cm/E♭
Dm7(♭5)
mf
55 Fm
Cm/E♭
Dm7(♭5)
58
Cm
Dm
mp
f
61 Cm/E♭
Fm
Cm
Dm
65 Cm/E♭
Gm
mf cresc.
ff
f
70
f
74
E♭/G
Gm6
E♭/G
Gm
f
f
80 E♭/G
Gm6
E♭/G
Gm
E♭/G
Gm6
E♭/G
Gm
E♭/G
Gm6
E♭/G
pp
91 Gm
E♭/G
Gm6
E♭/G
Repeat to fade
dim. poco a poco

Dancing With The Bear
(from 'Finding Neverland')

Music by Jan A.P. Kaczmarek

© Copyright 2005 MRX Music Corporation, USA.
All Rights Reserved. International Copyright Secured.

37
43
p
48
53
mp
58
espressivo
64
70
mf
75

Miller's Crossing (End Titles)
(from 'Miller's Crossing')

Music by Carter Burwell

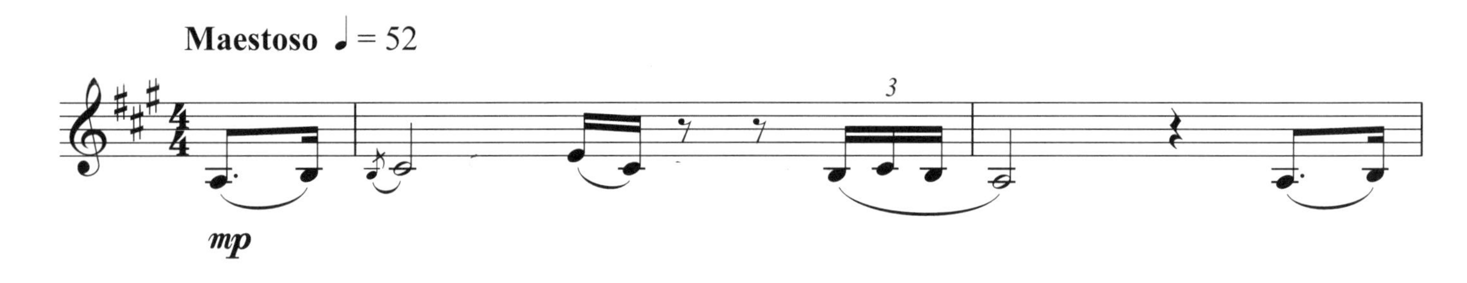

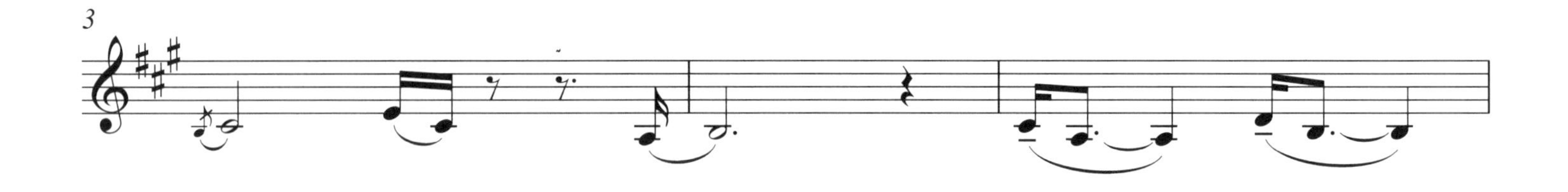

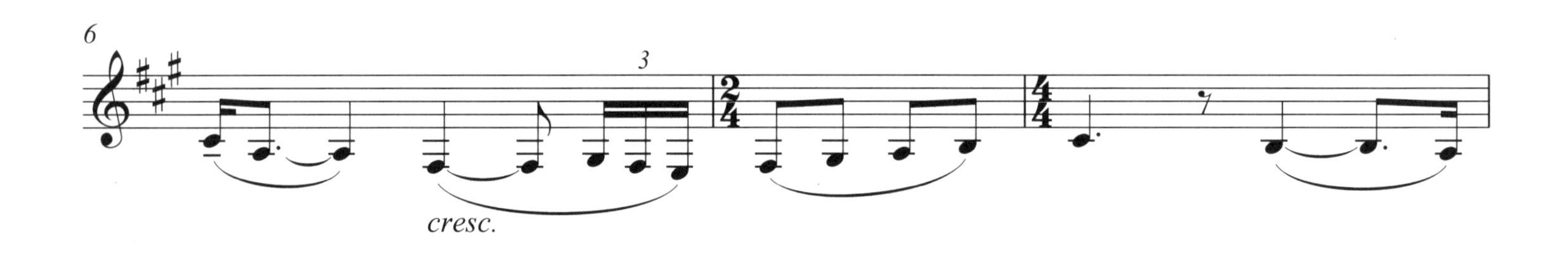

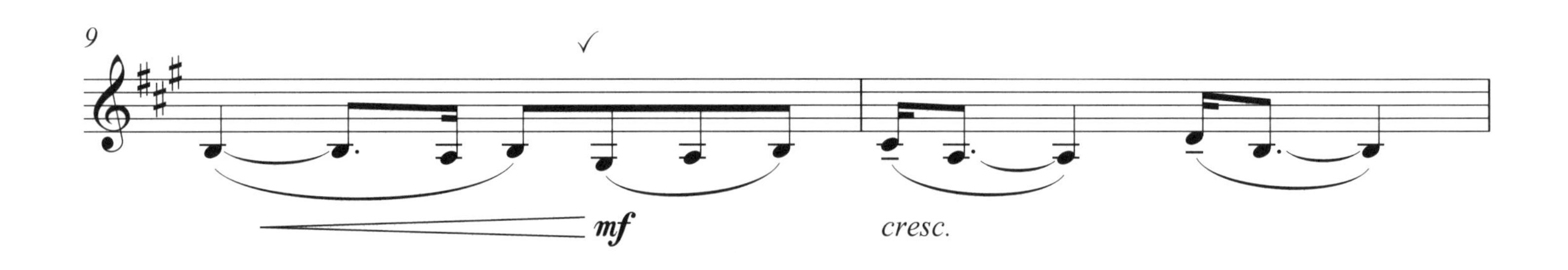

© Copyright 1990 TCF Music Publishing Incorporated, USA.
Used by permission of Hal Leonard Corporation.
All Rights Reserved. International Copyright Secured.

15

18
mf

22
mp

25
f

29
3
f

Eye Of The Tiger
(from 'Rocky III')

Words & Music by Frank Sullivan III & Jim Peterik

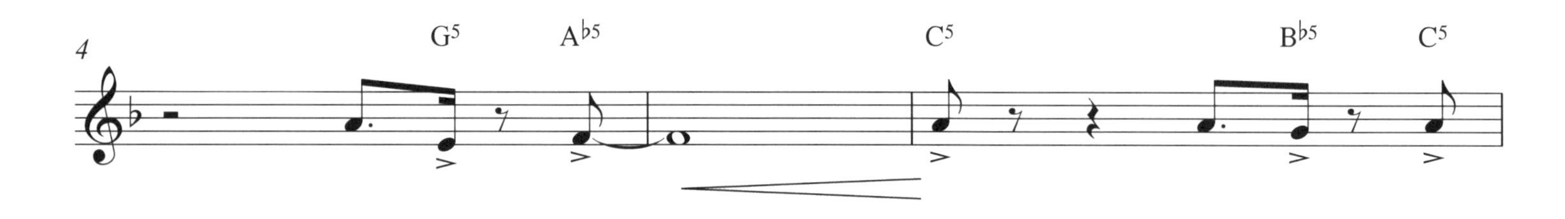

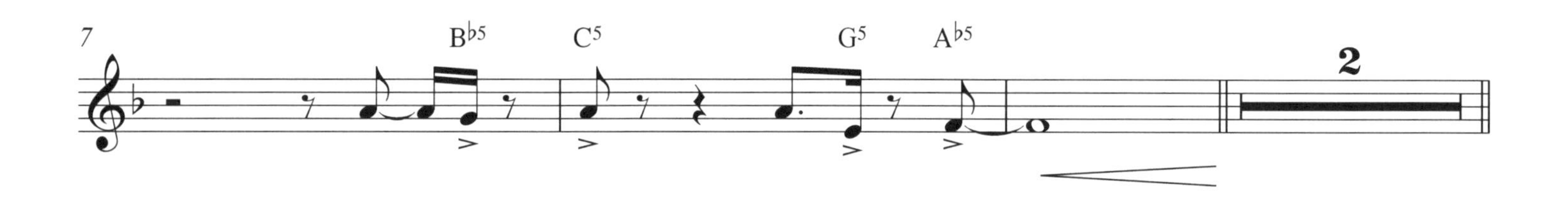

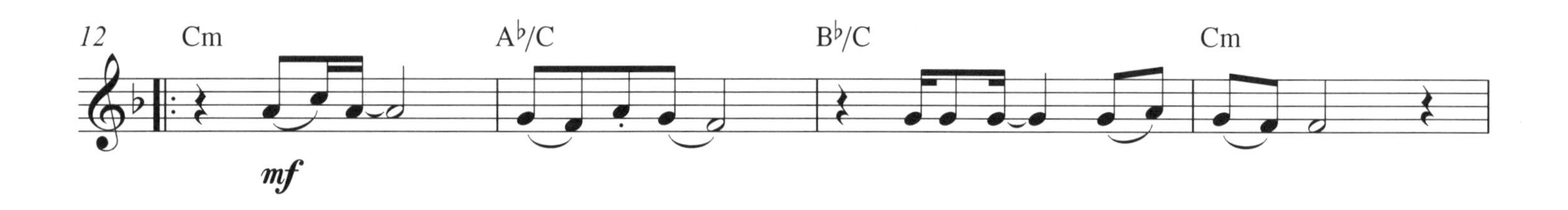

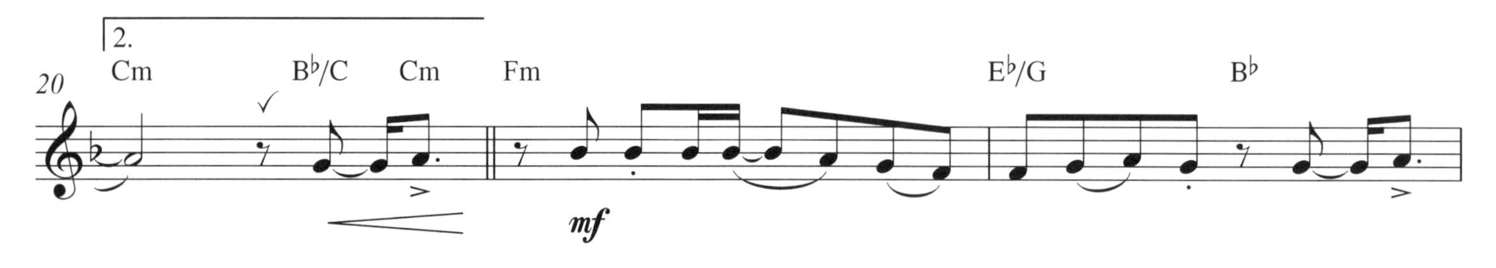

© Copyright 1982 Rude Music Incorporated/Ensign Music Corporation/Famous Music Corporation (50%)/Warner/Chappell Music Limited (50%).
All Rights Reserved. International Copyright Secured.

23
Fm
Cm7
B♭
Fm
26
E♭/G
B♭
Fm
E♭/G
A♭
N.C.
C5
f
mf
31
Cm
A♭/C
B♭/C
Cm
mp (2° mf)
35
A♭/C
B♭/C
38
Cm
B♭/C
Cm
Fm
E♭/G
B♭
mf (2° f)
41
Fm
Cm7
B♭
Fm
1.
44
E♭/G
B♭
Fm
E♭/G
A♭
f
2.
47
C5
A♭
C5
ff
mf

Georgia On My Mind
(from 'Ray')

Words by Stuart Gorrell & Music by Hoagy Carmichael

© Copyright 1930 Southern Music Publishing Company Incorporated, USA.
Campbell Connelly & Company Limited.
All Rights Reserved. International Copyright Secured.

29 F A7/E A7 Dm F7/C
32 B♭ Bdim7 F/C D7aug5 G9 C13(♭9) F B♭7
mp
36 F A7 Dm Gm Dm B♭7 Dm Gm Dm G7
mf
41 Dm Gm Dm Dm/C E7/B♭ E7 Am7 B♭/A♭
44 G7aug5 C F A7/E
mp mf mp
47 Dm F7/C B♭ Bdim7 F D7aug5 D7 G(add 9) B♭/C C7(♭9)
mf mp
51 E♭7(♯11) D(add 9) G(add 9)
mp
54 B♭/C F B♭ Bdim F G♭7 F F7(♯9)
mf

A Hard Day's Night
(from 'A Hard Day's Night')

Words & Music by John Lennon & Paul McCartney

© Copyright 1964 Sony/ATV Music Publishing (UK) Limited.
All Rights Reserved. International Copyright Secured.

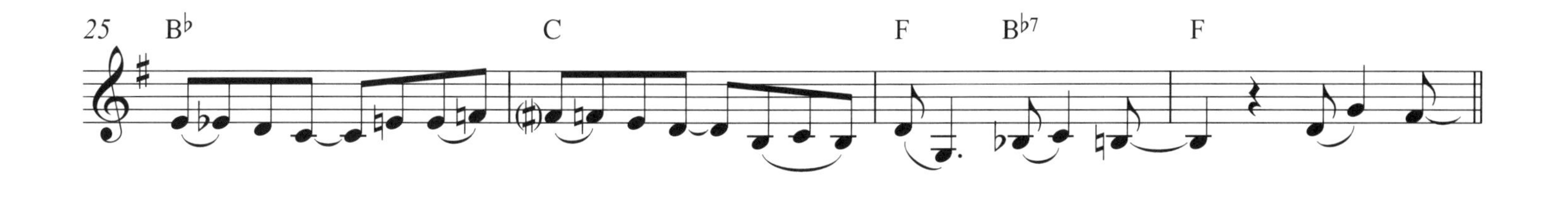
25
B♭
C
F
B♭7
F

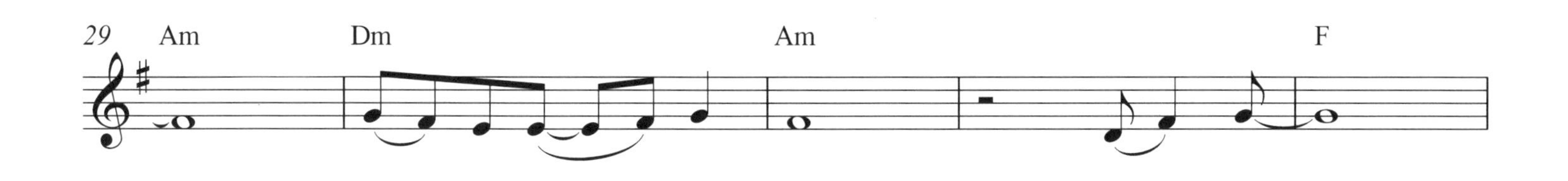
29
Am
Dm
Am
F

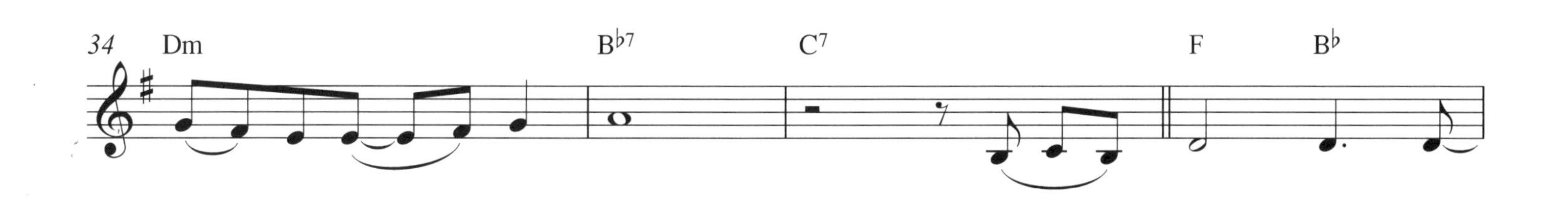
34
Dm
B♭7
C7
F
B♭

38
F
E♭
F

41
B♭
F
E♭
F

45
B♭
C
F
B♭7
F

Slower
49
B♭7
F
B♭
F

He's A Pirate

.ates Of The Caribbean: The Curse Of The Black Pearl')

Music by Klaus Badelt

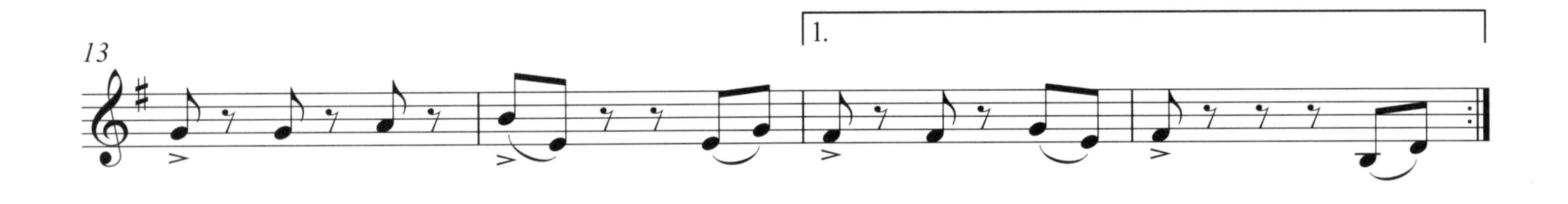

© Copyright 2004 Walt Disney Music Company, USA.
All Rights Reserved. International Copyright Secured.

29
33
f allargando
37
41
45
50
ff
56
61

Honor Him/Now We Are Free
(from 'Gladiator')

Music by Hans Zimmer

HONOR HIM

Noble and grand ♩ = 66

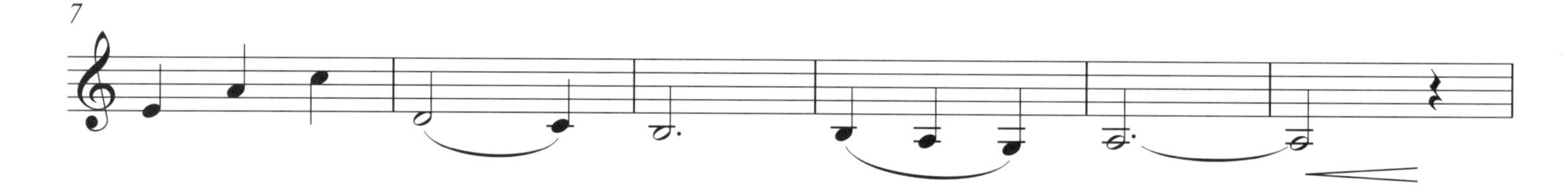

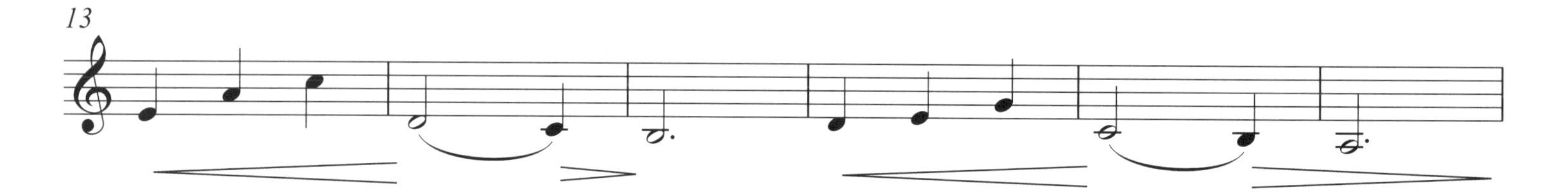

NOW WE ARE FREE

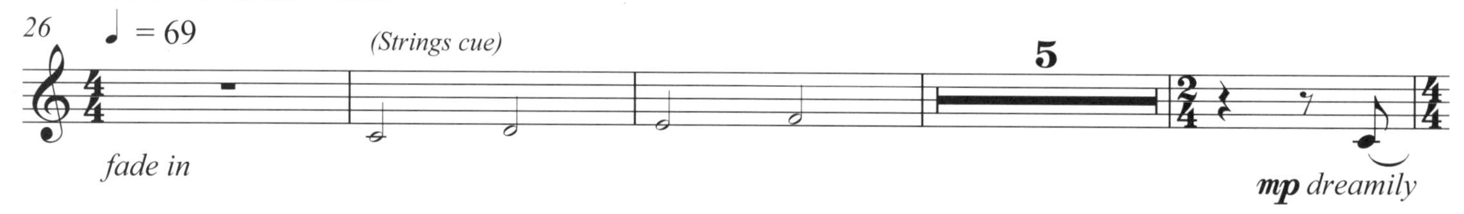

"Honor Him"
© Copyright 2000 SKG Music Publishing LLC/Cherry Lane Music Publishing Company, USA (75%)/Universal/MCA Music Limited (25%).
All rights in Germany administered by Universal/MCA Music Publ. GmbH. All Rights Reserved. International Copyright Secured.

"Now We Are Free"
© Copyright 2000 SKG Music Publishing LLC/Cherry Lane Music Publishing Company, USA (87.5%)/Universal/MCA Music Limited (12.5%).
All rights in Germany administered by Universal/MCA Music Publ. GmbH. All Rights Reserved. International Copyright Secured.

42
mf
46
50
54
58
f more rhythmically
63
68
73

I Had A Farm In Africa
(Main Title from 'Out Of Africa')

Music by John Barry

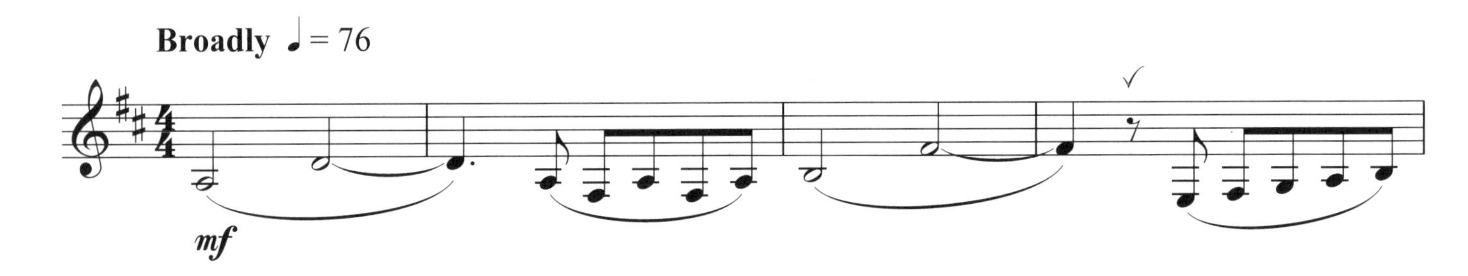

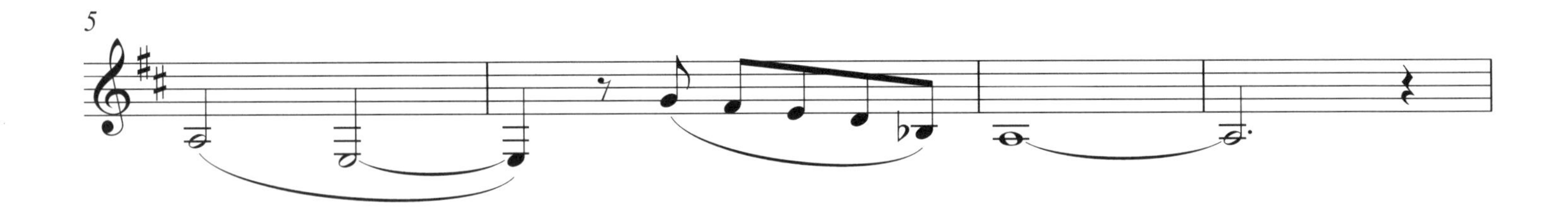

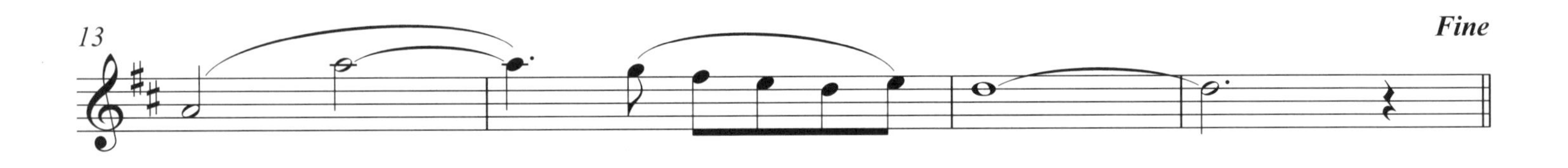

© Copyright 1985 Music Corporation Of America Incorporated, USA.
Universal/MCA Music Limited.
All rights in Germany administered by Universal/MCA Music Publ. GmbH.
All Rights Reserved. International Copyright Secured.

Into The West
(from 'The Lord Of The Rings: The Return Of The King')

Words & Music by Annie Lennox, Howard Shore & Fran Walsh

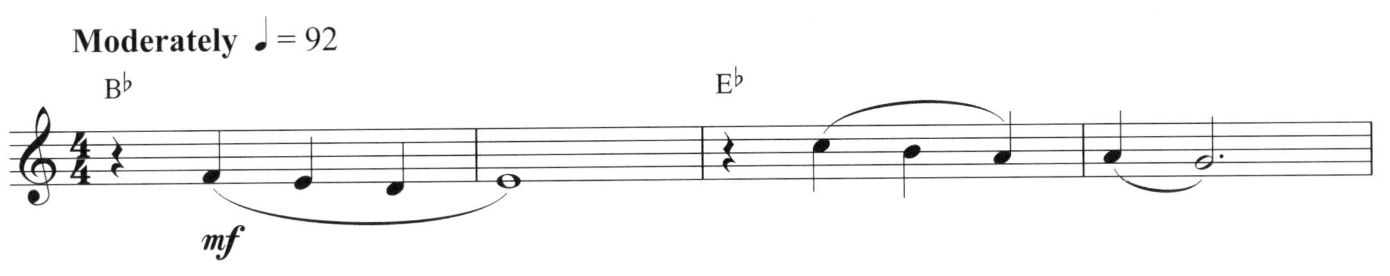

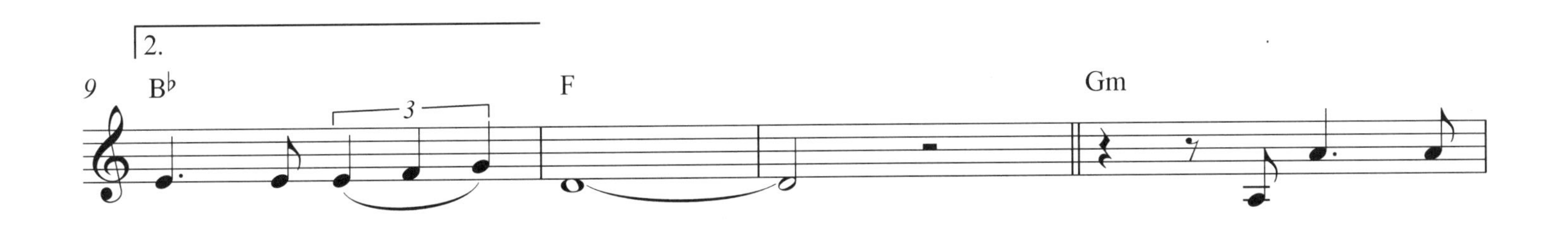

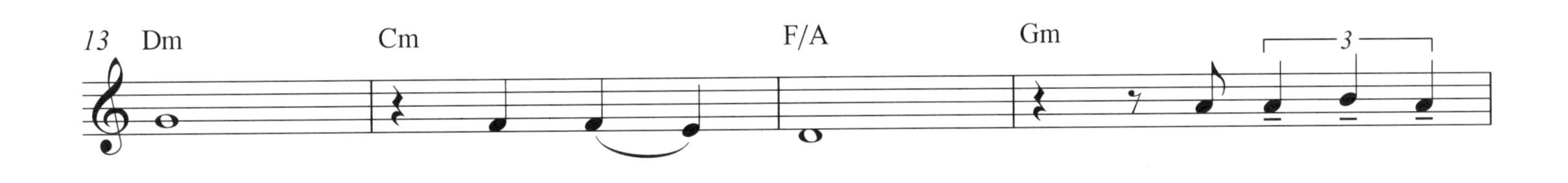

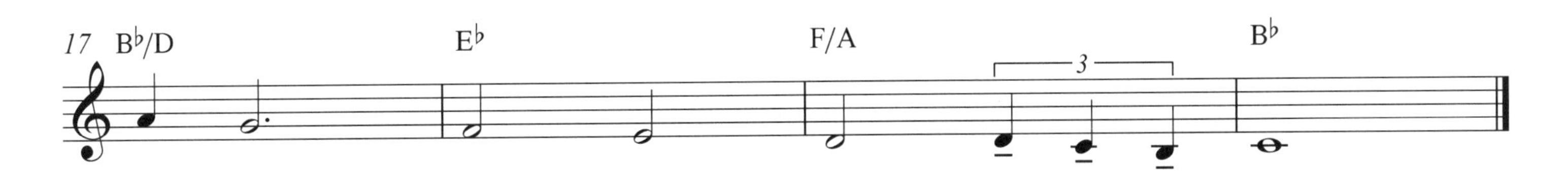

© Copyright 2003 La Lennoxa Music Company Limited/South Fifth Avenue Publishing/New Line Tunes, USA.
Sony/ATV Music Publishing (UK) Limited(8.33%)/Warner/Chappell Music Limited (58.34%)/Universal Music Publishing MGB Limited (33.33%).
All Rights in Germany Administered by Musik Edition Discoton GmbH (A Division of Universal Music Publishing Group).
All Rights Reserved. International Copyright Secured.

(I've Had) The Time Of My Life
(from 'Dirty Dancing')

Words & Music by Frankie Previte, John DeNicola & Donald Markowitz

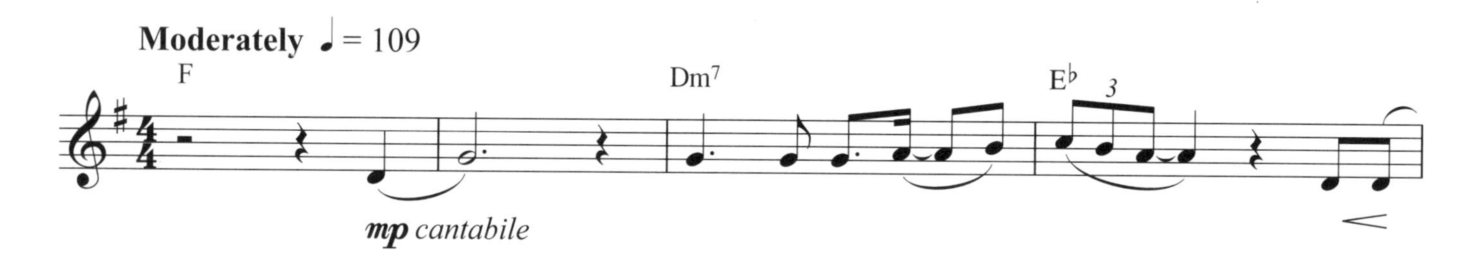

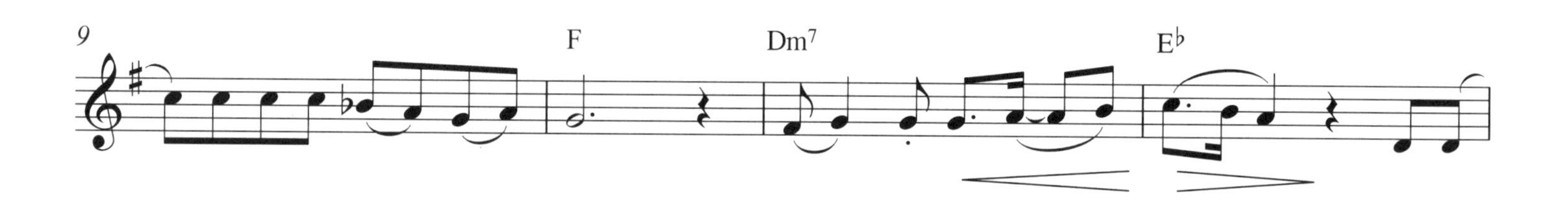

© Copyright 1987 Sony/ATV Music Publishing (UK) Limited (12.5%)/EMI Music Publishing Limited (25%)/Worldsong Incorporated (62.5%).
All Rights Reserved. International Copyright Secured.

Eb/F
F
Eb/F
mf
F
Bb7
mf
mp legato
Ab
Bb7
Csus4
C
F
Dm7
f
Eb
F
Dm7
To Coda
Eb
Gm
C7
F
Bb/F
mf

53
E♭/F
3
F
3
mp animato

57
E♭/F
3
F

61
E♭/F
F
cresc. poco a poco

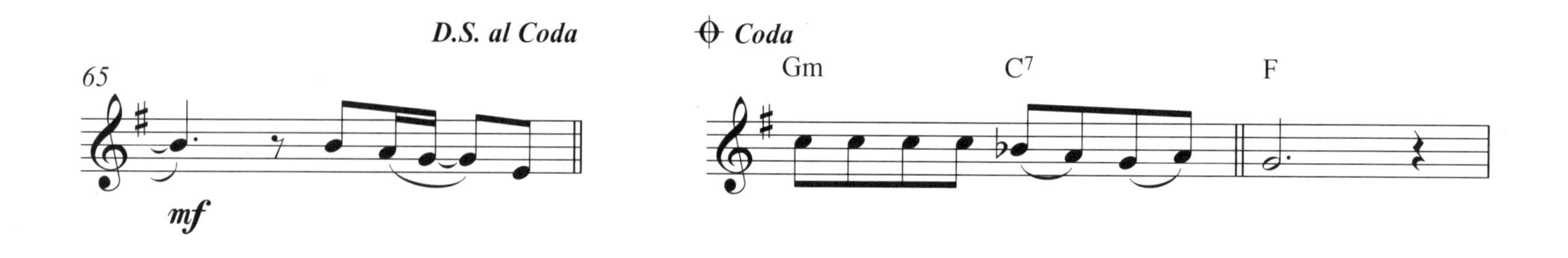
D.S. al Coda
Coda
65
Gm
C7
F
mf

68
Dm7
3
E♭
3
F

72
Dm7
E♭
3
C7
F

Lawrence Of Arabia (Main Titles)
(from 'Lawrence Of Arabia')

Music by Maurice Jarre

© Copyright 1962 Gower Music Incorporated, USA.
Shapiro Bernstein & Company Limited.
All Rights Reserved. International Copyright Secured.

Le Banquet/La Valse Des Monstres
(from 'Amélie')

Music by Yann Tiersen

© Copyright 1995 Ici, d'ailleursà/Sony Music Publishing, France.
Sony/ATV Music Publishing (UK) Limited.
All Rights Reserved. International Copyright Secured.

49
mp
56
63
mf
69
75
LA VALSE DES MONSTRES
A little faster
81
88
96

104
112
120
129
136
To Coda
145
2
mp
151
155
mf

1.
2.
D.S. al Coda
Coda
160
166
mp
171
175
180
1.
2.
186
(Play 6 times)
f
192
1-5.
199
6.
molto rit.

Licence To Kill
(from 'Licence To Kill')

Words & Music by John Barry, Leslie Bricusse, Anthony Newley, Narada Michael Walden, Walter Afanasieff & Jeffrey Cohen

© Copyright 1989 Gratitude Sky Music Incorporated/Penzafire Music/Sony ATV Songs LLC/U-A Music International Incorporated, USA.
Sony/ATV Music Publishing (UK) Limited.
All Rights Reserved. International Copyright Secured.

22
f espressivo

25

29

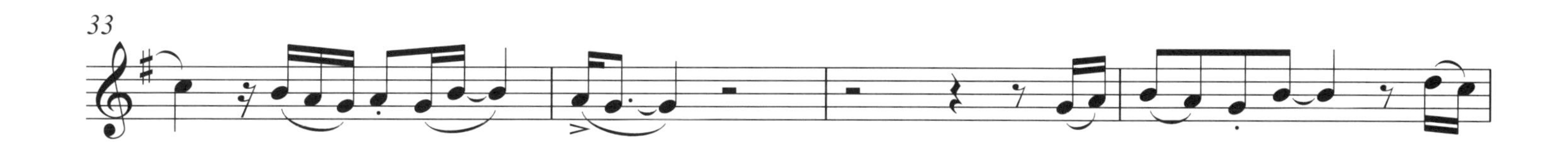
33

37

40
mf ritmico

43

molto rit.
A tempo
molto rit.

Live To Tell
(from 'At Close Range')

Words & Music by Madonna Ciccone & Pat Leonard

© Copyright 1986 WB Music Corporation/Webo Girl Publishing Incorporated/Bleu Disque Music Company Incorporated/Johnny Yuma Music, USA.
Sony/ATV Music Publishing (UK) Limited (25%)/Warner/Chappell Music Limited (50%)/EMI Music Publishing Limited (25%).
All Rights Reserved. International Copyright Secured.

38
Cm
E♭sus4
E♭
mf
42
E♭sus4
Gm
A♭
E♭
45
Cm
A♭/C
B♭/D
Cm
B♭
A♭
f
Rubato, slower
49
Cm
54
B♭/C
A tempo
A♭
mf
59
B♭
Cm
Gm7
A♭
63
B♭
Gm7
A♭
67
B♭
Cm
Gm7
A♭

71
B♭
Cm
B♭
E♭
Fm
B♭
mf
78
E♭sus4
E♭
E♭sus4
81
Gm
A♭
E♭
Cm
A♭/C
B♭/D
85
Cm
B♭
A♭
B♭
Cm
mf
89
E♭sus4
E♭
E♭sus4
92
Gm
A♭
E♭
Cm
A♭/C
B♭/D
Fade to end
96
Cm
B♭
A♭
B♭
Cm
f

A Love Before Time
(from 'Crouching Tiger, Hidden Dragon')

Words & Music by James Schamus, Tan Dun & Jorge Calandrelli

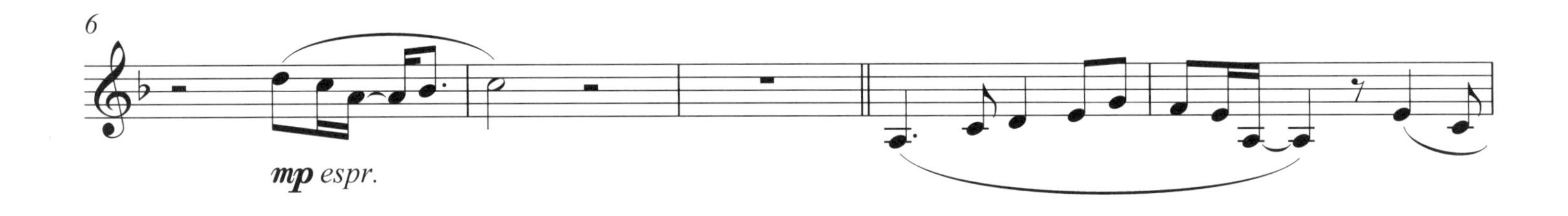

© Copyright 2000 Sony/ATV Tunes LLC/Symbolic Exchange Incorporated/ParnassusProductions Incorporated, USA.
Sony/ATV Music Publishing (UK) Limited.
All Rights Reserved. International Copyright Secured.

26
2
31
molto
35
40
molto
f
44
lightly
47
mf
50
53
mp

Love Is All Around
(from 'Four Weddings And A Funeral')

Words & Music by Reg Presley

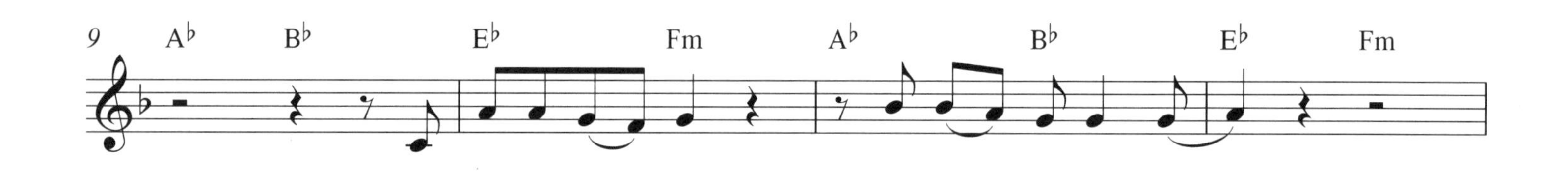

© Copyright 1967 Dick James Music Limited. Universal/Dick James Music Limited.
All rights in Germany administered by Universal Music Publ. GmbH.
All Rights Reserved. International Copyright Secured.

24
B♭
1.
2.
28
B♭7
E♭
Fm
31
A♭
B♭
E♭
Fm
A♭
B♭
34
E♭
Fm
A♭
B♭
E♭
Fm
37
A♭
B♭
E♭
Fm
A♭
B♭
40
E♭
Fm
A♭
B♭
E♭
Fm
A♭
B♭
44
E♭
Fm
A♭
B♭
A♭
B♭
E♭

A Man And A Woman
(from 'Un Homme et une Femme')

Words by Pierre Barouh & Music by Francis Lai. English Translation by Jerry Keller

© Copyright 1966 Editions Saravah, France.
Universal/MCA Music Limited.
All rights in Germany administered by Universal/MCA Music Publ. GmbH.
All Rights Reserved. International Copyright Secured.

28
Gm7
C7
Fmaj7
N.C.
(Straight quavers)
32
Fmaj7
36
E7
E♭maj7
40
Am7
D7
1.
2.
44
Gmaj7
G6
N.C.
Am7
49
D7
Gmaj7
Am7
53
Gmaj7
G♭maj7
57
Fmaj7
G♭maj7
Gmaj7

Mothersbaugh's Canon
(from 'The Royal Tenenbaums')

Music by Mark Mothersbaugh

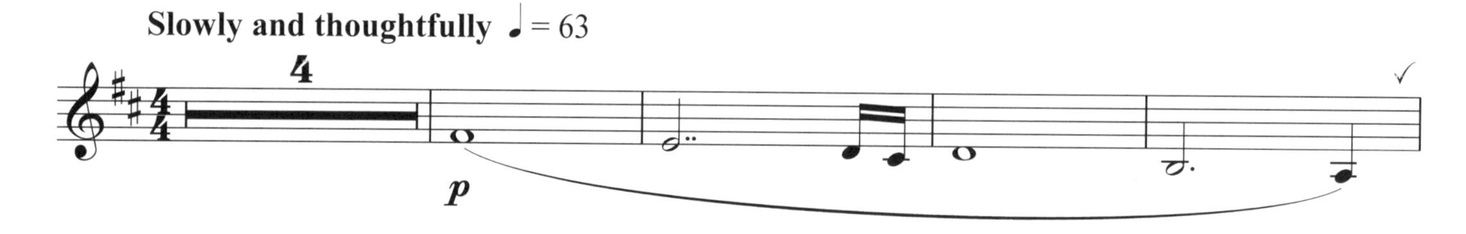

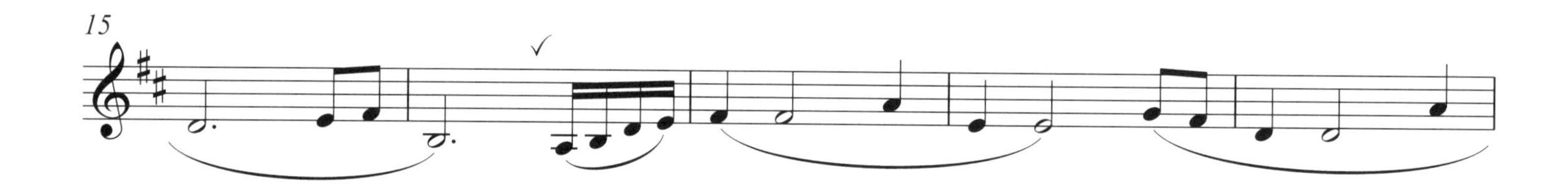

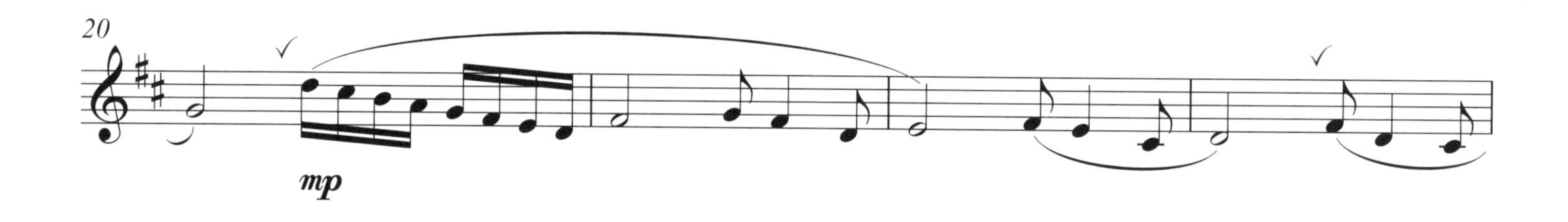

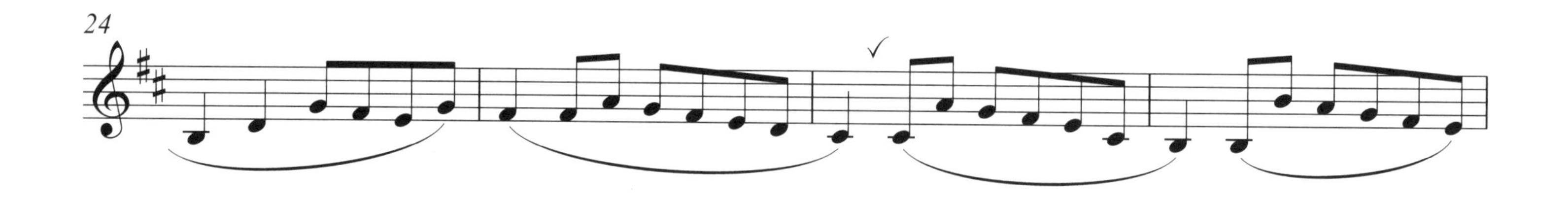

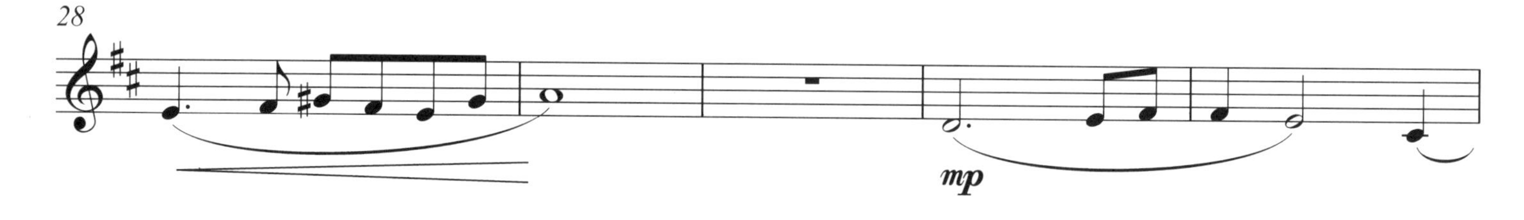

© Copyright 2001 Buena Vista Music Company, USA.
All Rights Reserved. International Copyright Secured.

33
cresc.
37
mf
39
41
43
45
dim.
48
rit.
p

Nothing's Gonna Stop Us Now
(from 'Mannequin')

Words & Music by Diane Warren & Albert Hammond

© Copyright 1986, 1987 Realsongs/Albert Hammond Enterprises Incorporated, USA/Edition Sunset Publishing Incorporated
EMI Music Publishing Limited (31.25%)/P and P Songs Limited (50%)/Universal Music Publishing MGB Limited (18.75%).
All Rights in Germany Administered by Musik Edition Discoton GmbH (A Division of Universal Music Publishing Group).
All Rights Reserved. International Copyright Secured.

Oh, Pretty Woman
(from 'Pretty Woman')

Words & Music by Roy Orbison & Bill Dees

© Copyright 1964 (renewed 1992) Acuff Rose Music Incorporated/Roy Orbison Music Company/Barbara Orbison Music Company, USA.
P & P Songs Limited (50%)/Acuff-Rose Music Limited (50%).
All Rights Reserved. International Copyright Secured.

Once Upon A Time In The West
(from 'Once Upon A Time In The West')

Music by Ennio Morricone

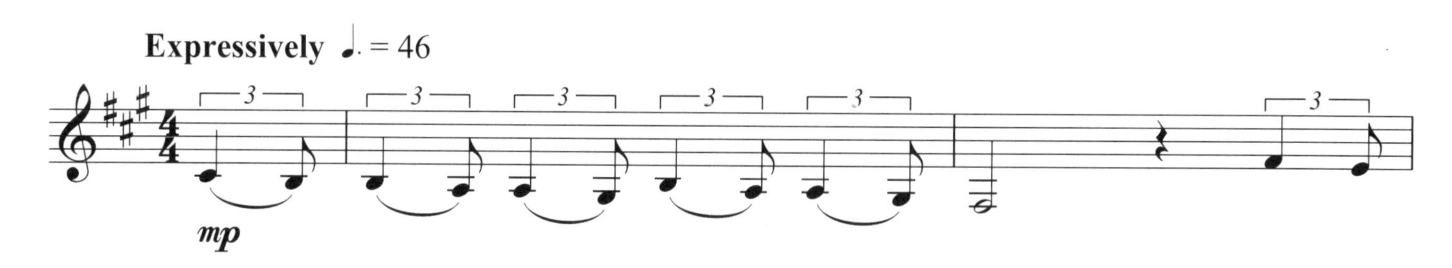

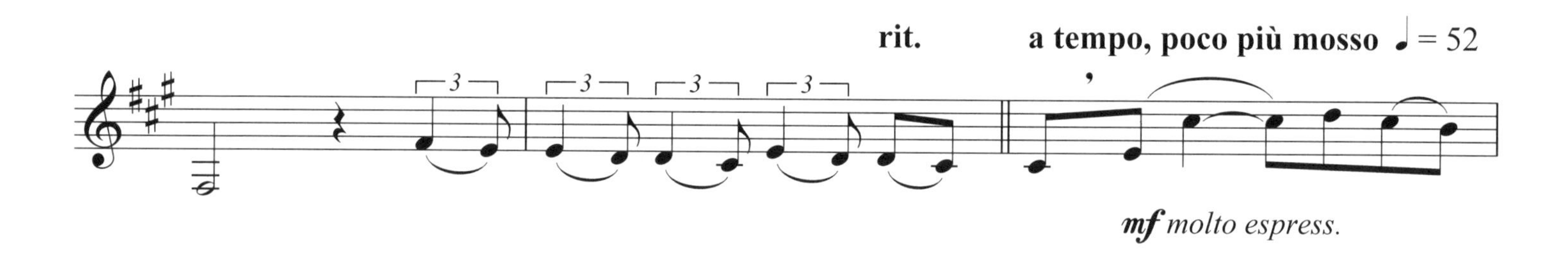

© Copyright 1968 Famous Music Corporation, USA.
All Rights Reserved. International Copyright Secured.

13
molto rit.
a tempo, con moto ♩ = 52
mf molto espress.

17

21
f

25

29
mp

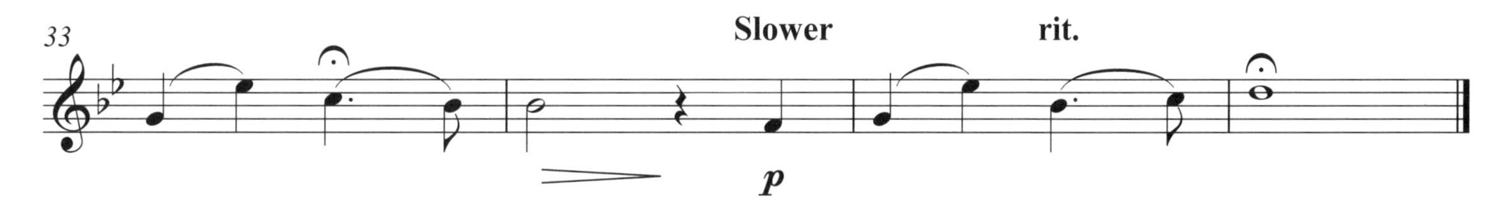

33
Slower
rit.
p

Passage Of Time/Vianne Sets Up Shop
(from The Miramax Motion Picture 'Chocolat')

Music by Rachel Portman

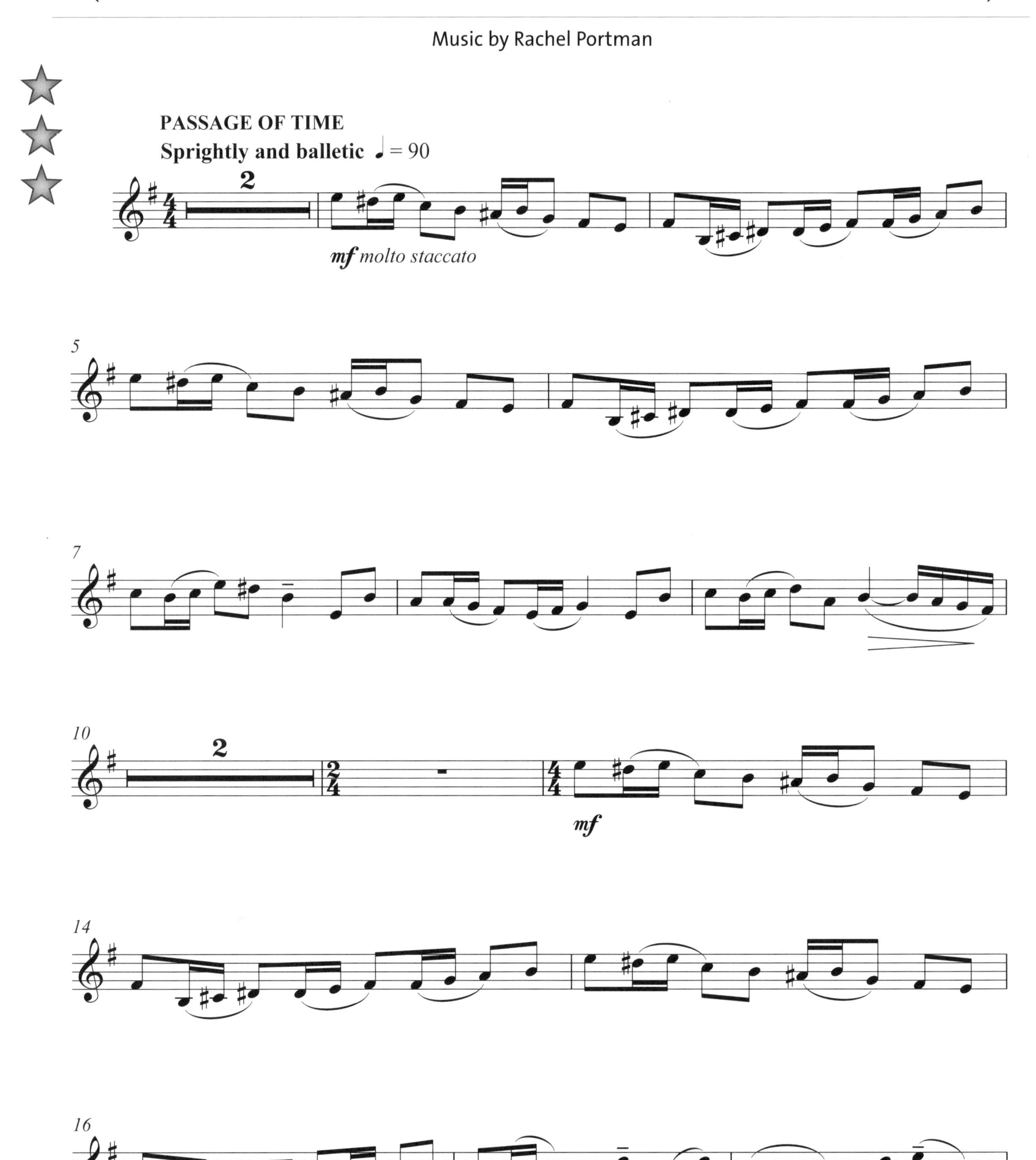

© Copyright 2000 Miramax Film Music, USA.
All Rights Reserved. International Copyright Secured.

19
p cresc.
22
mf
25
mf legato
30
rall.
34
a tempo
2
mf staccato again
39
mf
43
as though fading
47
2
dim.

52
VIANNE SETS UP SHOP
Folkdance-like ♩ = 106
58
f staccato
62
65
69
73
77
80

83
86
89
92
95
98
102
sfp
105

Pelagia's Song
(from 'Captain Corelli's Mandolin')

Music by Stephen Warbeck

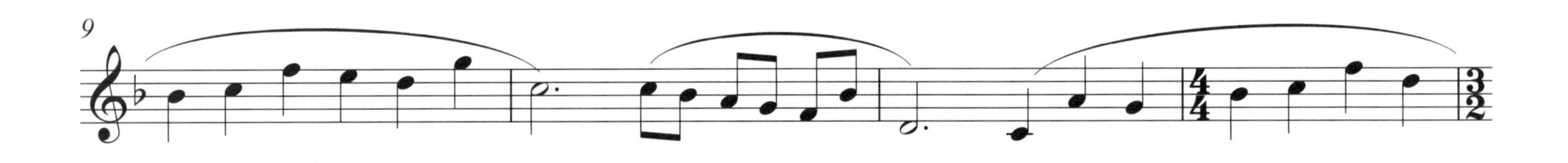

© Copyright 2001 Universal Music Publishing Limited.
All rights in Germany administered by Universal Music Publ. GmbH.
All Rights Reserved. International Copyright Secured.

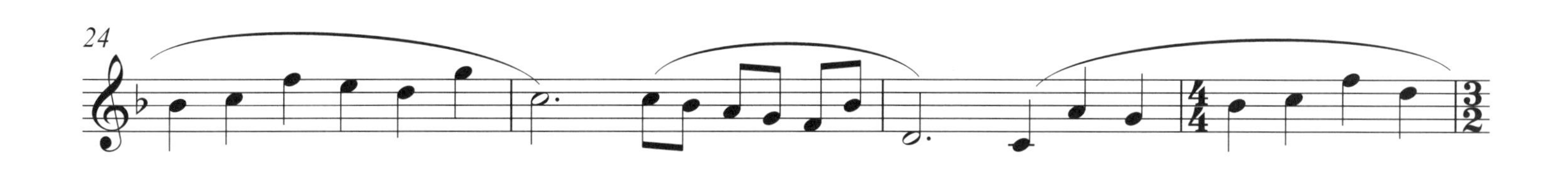
24
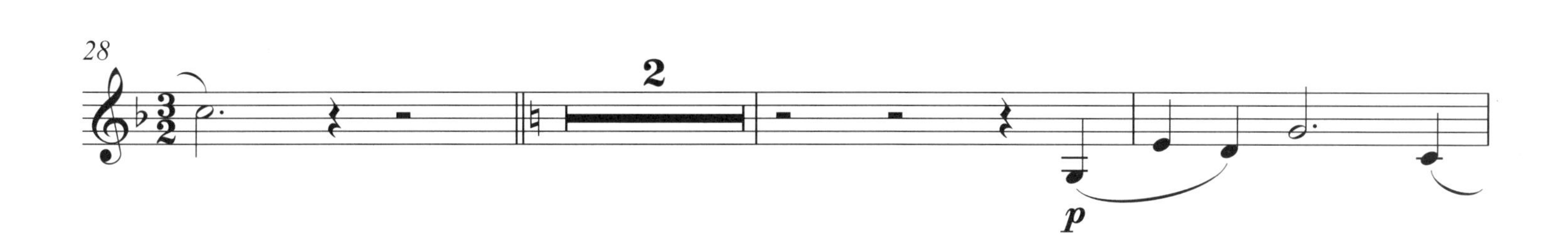
28
2
p
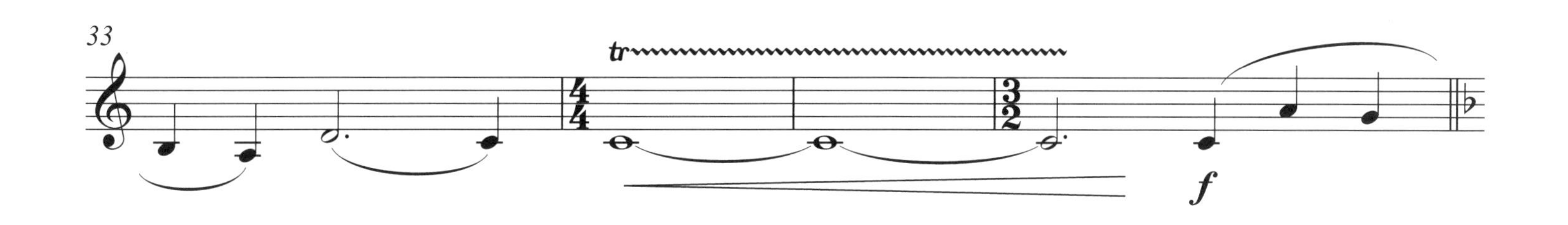
33
tr
f
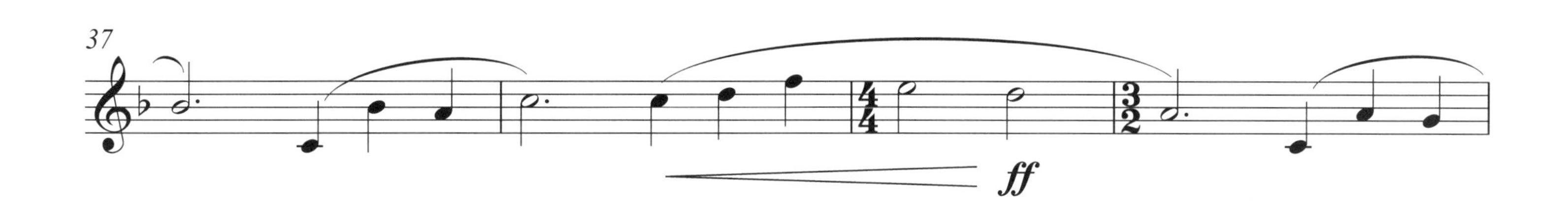
37
ff
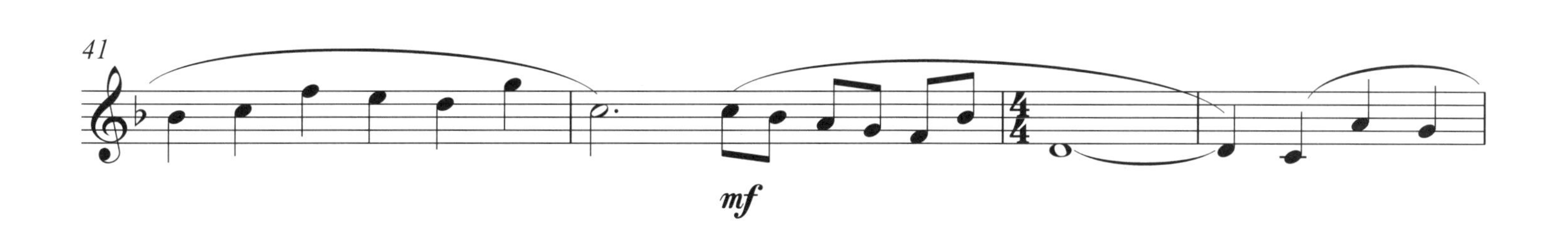
41
mf
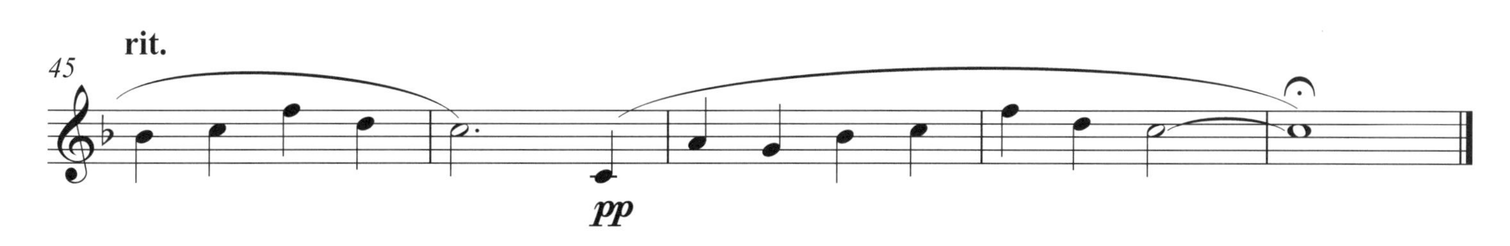
rit.
45
pp

Pelle Erobreren
(from 'Pelle The Conqueror')

Music by Stefan Nilsson

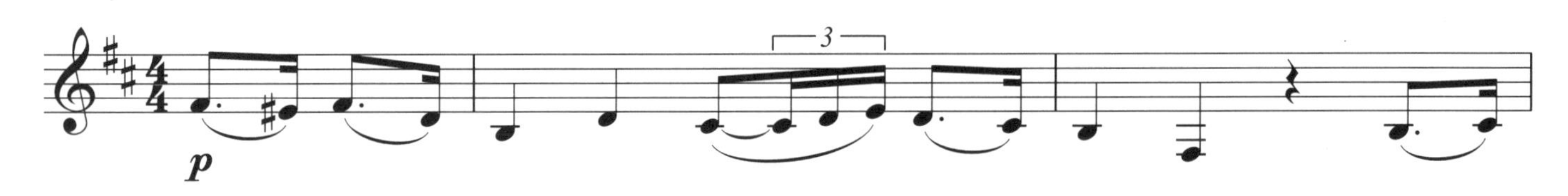

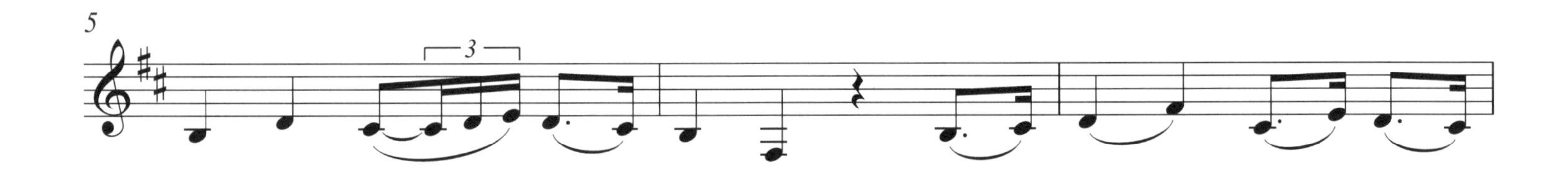

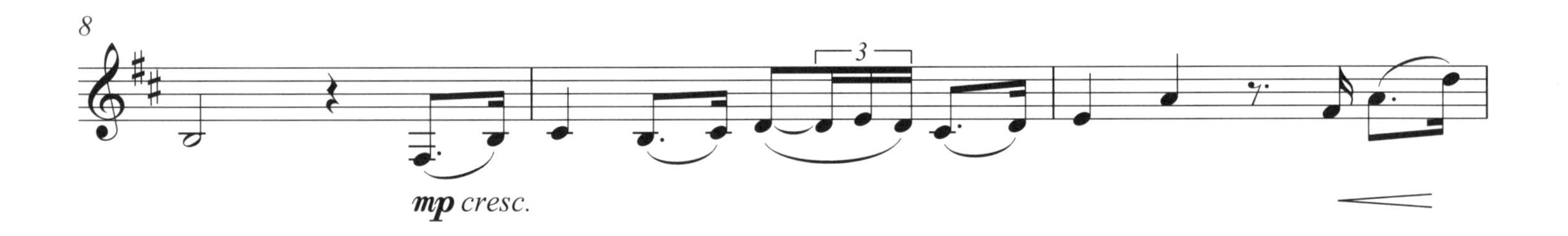

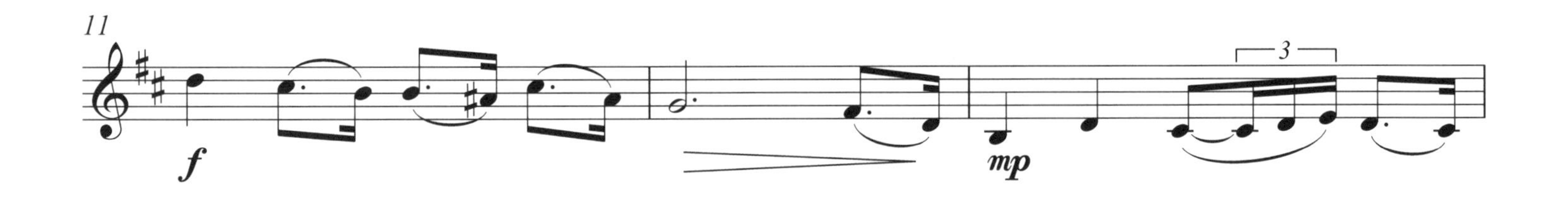

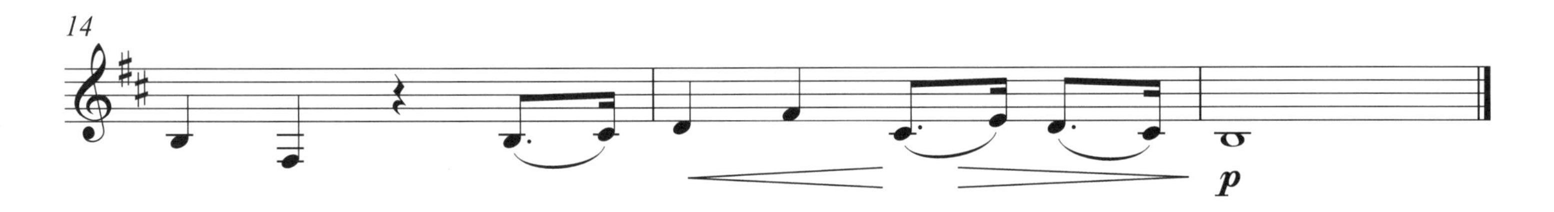

© Copyright 1987 Copyright Control.
All Rights Reserved. International Copyright Secured.

Prologue: My Life Before Me
(from 'The Portrait Of A Lady')

Music by Wojciech Kilar

© Copyright 1997 Songs Of PolyGram International Incorporated, USA.
Universal Music Publishing Limited.
All rights in Germany administered by Universal Music Publ. GmbH.
All Rights Reserved. International Copyright Secured.

PM's Love Theme
(from 'Love Actually')

Words & Music by Craig Armstrong

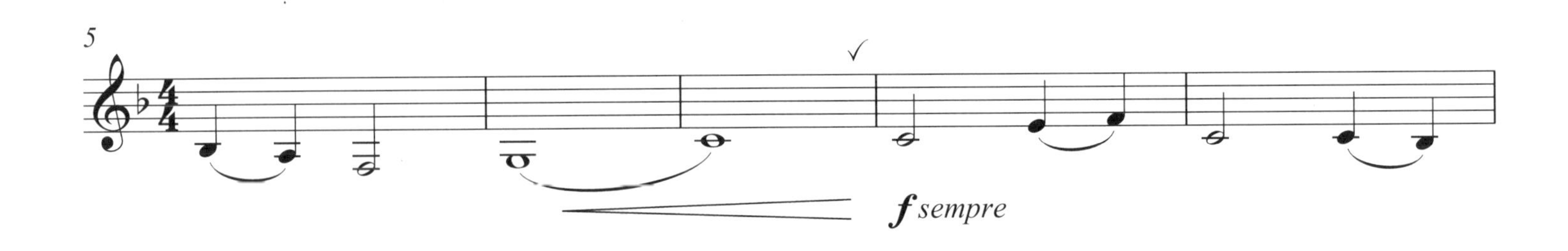

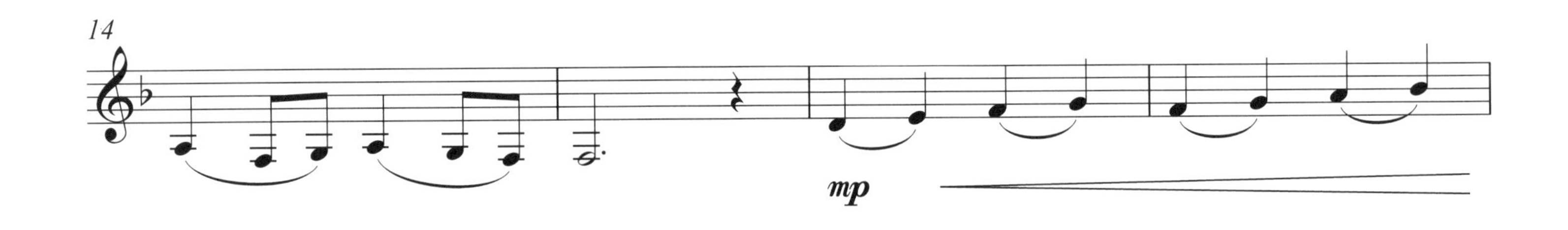

© Copyright 2003 Universal Pictures Music.
All Rights Reserved. International Copyright Secured.

22
mp cresc.

26
f

29

32
cresc. poco a poco

36
rit.
ff
mf
mp

The Promise
(from 'The Piano')

Music by Michael Nyman

© Copyright 1992 Michael Nyman Limited/Chester Music Limited.
All Rights Reserved. International Copyright Secured.

Schindler's List (Theme)
(from 'Schindler's List')

Music by John Williams

© Copyright 1993 Music Corporation of America Incorporated, USA.
Universal/MCA Music Limited.
All rights in Germany administered by Universal/MCA Music Publ. GmbH.
All Rights Reserved. International Copyright Secured.

Reprise...
(from 'Spirited Away')

Music by Joe Hisaishi

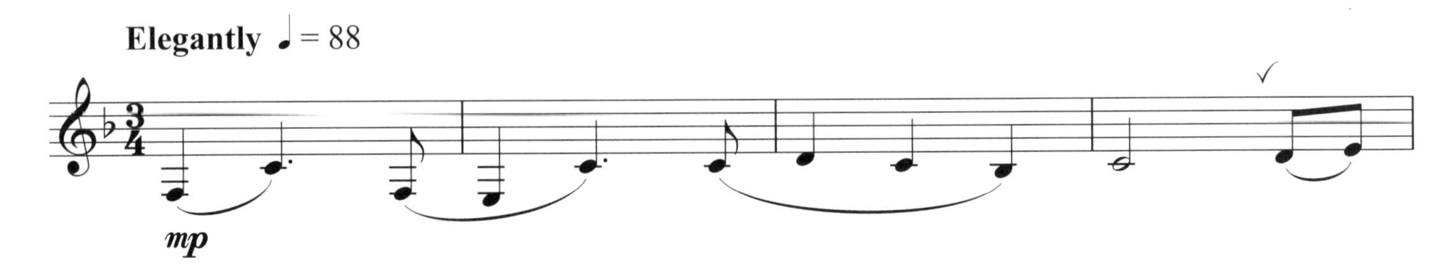

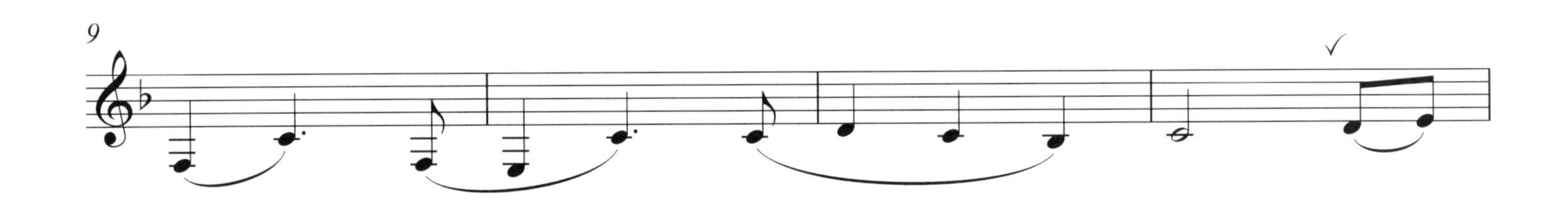

© Copyright 2001 Tokumo Shoten/Studio Ghibli, Japan.
Sony/ATV Music Publishing (UK) Limited.
All Rights Reserved. International Copyright Secured.

25
mp
29
33
f
37
mf
41
45
sempre f e legato
49
rit.

Rule The World
(from 'Stardust')

Words & Music by Mark Owen, Gary Barlow, Jason Orange & Howard Donald

© Copyright 2007 EMI Music Publishing Limited (50%)/Sony/ATV Music Publishing (UK) Limited (25%)/
Universal Music Publishing Limited (25%) (administered in Germany by Universal Music Publ. GmbH).
All Rights Reserved. International Copyright Secured.

32
Fm9
A♭maj7
E♭
35
B♭sus4
B♭
E♭
Cm
Gm
f
39
A♭
B♭
E♭
Cm
Gm
43
A♭
B♭
E♭
46
Cm
Gm
A♭
B♭
49
E♭
Cm
Gm
A♭
52
B♭
E♭
Cm
Gm
55
A♭
B♭
E♭
58
Cm
Gm
A♭
B♭
E♭

Scene D'Amour
(from 'Vertigo')

Music by Bernard Herrmann

© Copyright 1958 Famous Music Corporation, USA.
All Rights Reserved. International Copyright Secured.

33
mp
39
44
espressivo
49
54
mp
58
63
cresc.
67
ff

The Shower
(from 'Dressed To Kill')

Music by Pino Donaggio

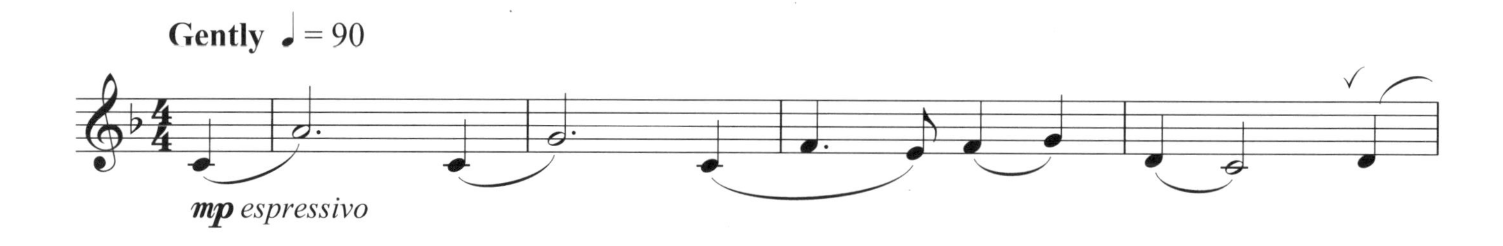

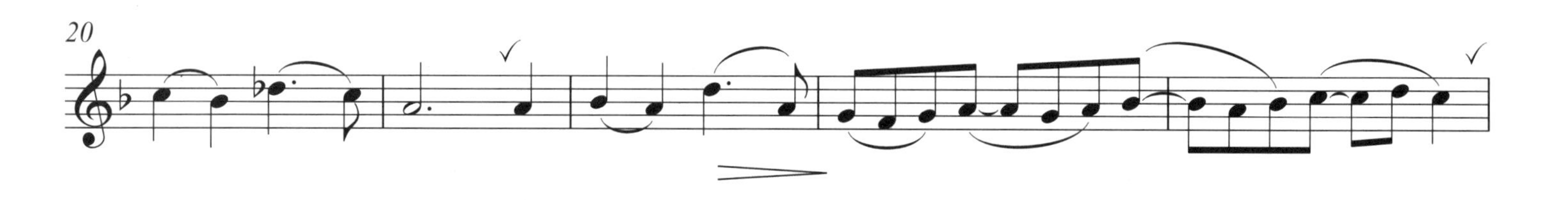

© Copyright 1980 Universal Music Publishing Limited.
All rights in Germany administered by Universal Music Publ. GmbH.
All Rights Reserved. International Copyright Secured.

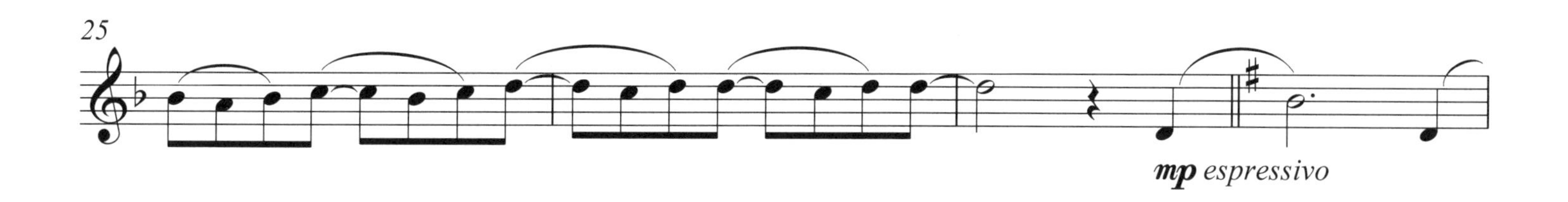
25
mp espressivo

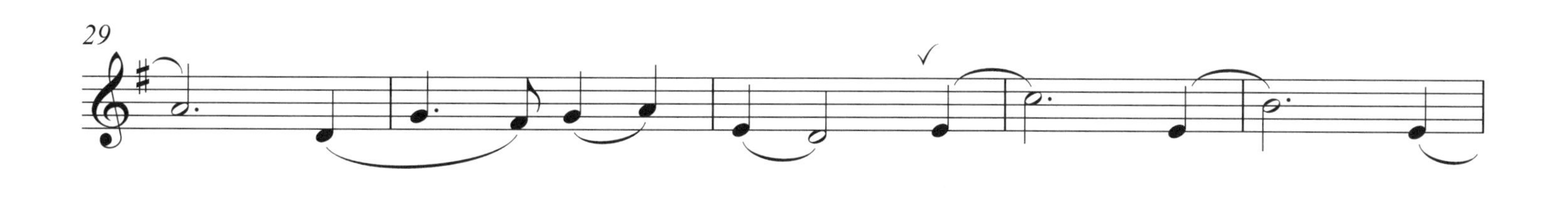
29

34
mf

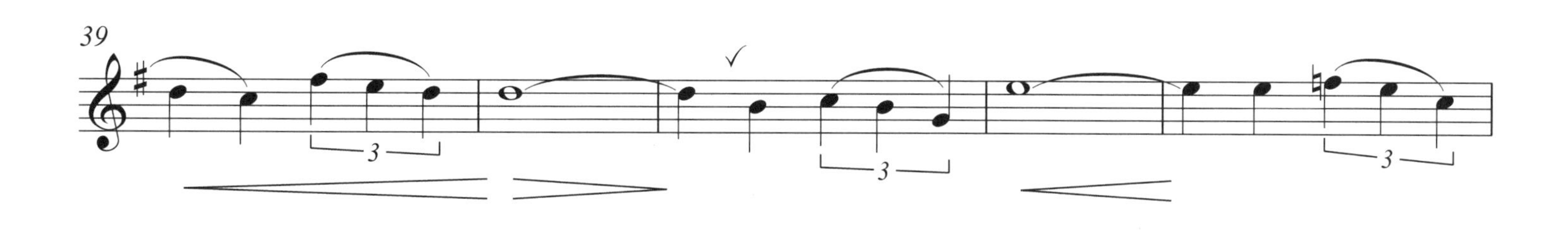
39
3
3
3

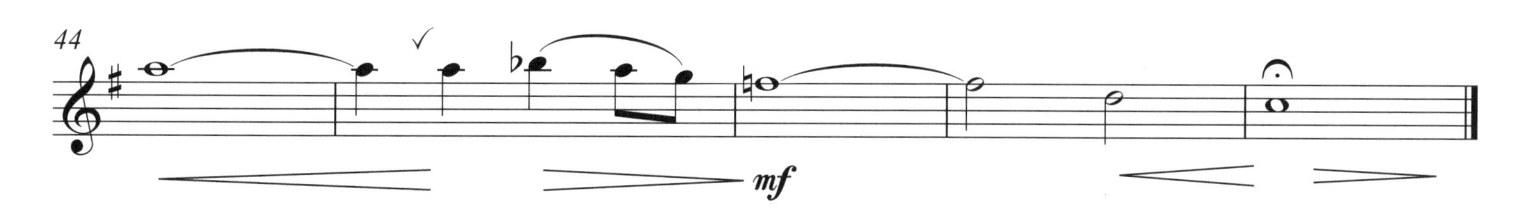
44
mf

The Sound Of Silence
(from 'The Graduate')

Words & Music by Paul Simon

© Copyright 1964 Paul Simon Music, USA.
All Rights Reserved. International Copyright Secured.

Top Gun (Anthem)
(from 'Top Gun')

Music by Harold Faltermeyer

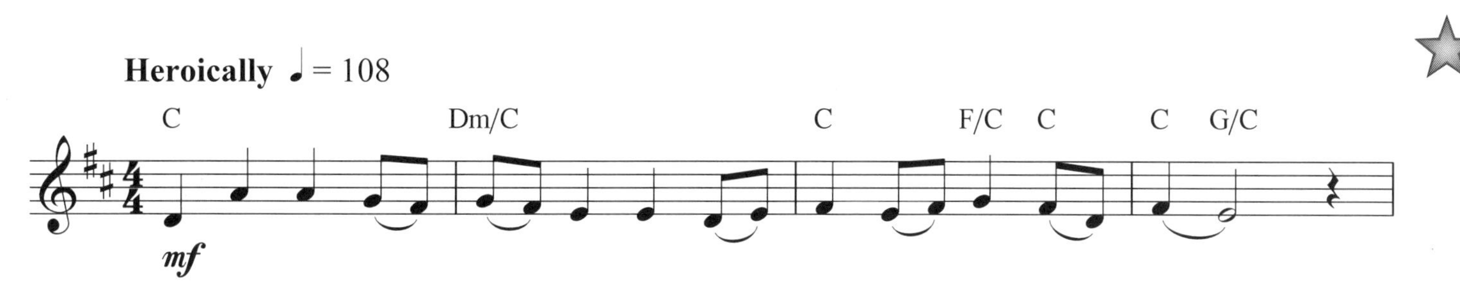

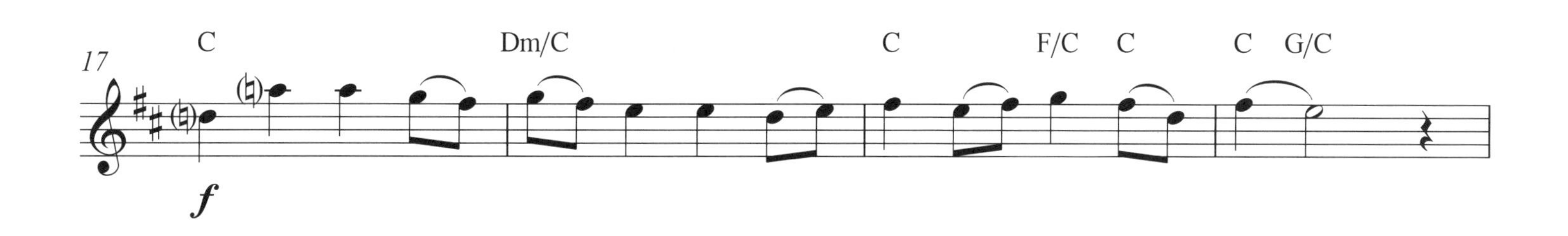

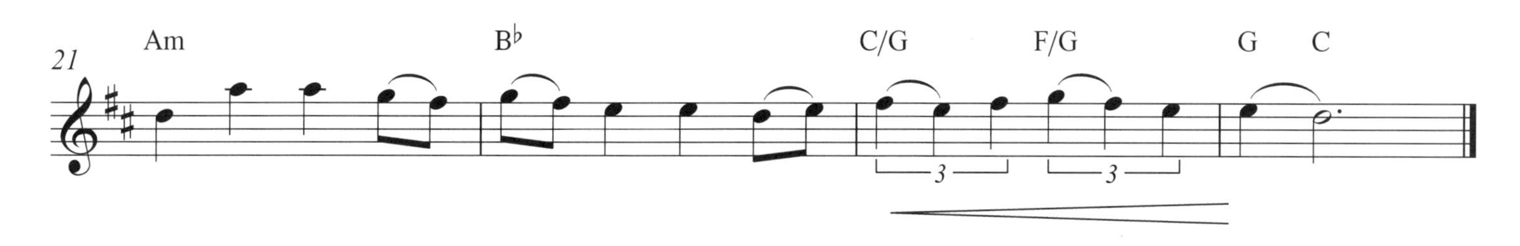

© Copyright 1981 Famous Music Publishing Limited.
All Rights Reserved. International Copyright Secured.

Sweets To The Sweet—Farewell
(from 'Hamlet')

Music by Patrick Doyle

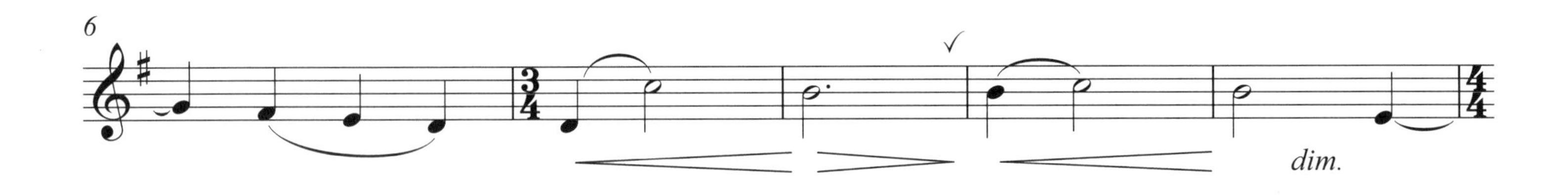

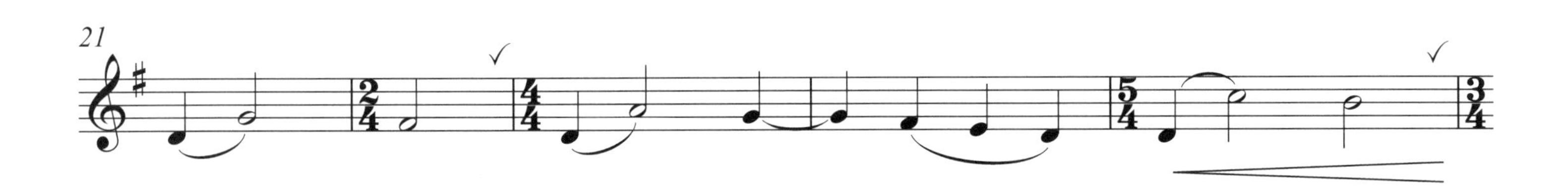

© Copyright 1996 Air Edel Associates Limited (50%)/Warner/Chappell Music North America (50%).
All Rights Reserved. International Copyright Secured.

Poco più mosso ♩ = c.76
rit. poco a poco
mf
pp dolce
A tempo ♩ = c.66
f
mp
f dim.
p molto espress.
p
pp

Try A Little Tenderness
(from 'The Commitments')

Words & Music by Harry Woods, Jimmy Campbell & Reg Connelly

© Copyright 1932 & 1960 Campbell Connelly & Company Limited.
All Rights Reserved. International Copyright Secured.

43 B♭ Gm Cm F7 B♭ A♭
3
49 G7 Cm F
55 B♭ G7
59 Cm B♭/D E♭ Edim F G♭ G A♭ A
63 B♭ A♭ G7
67 Cm B♭/D E♭ Edim F G♭ G A♭ A
71 B♭ A♭ G7 Cm B♭/D
rall.
76 E♭ Edim F G♭ G A♭ A B♭

Up Where We Belong
(from 'An Officer And A Gentleman')

Words & Music by Jack Nitzsche, Will Jennings & Buffy Sainte-Marie

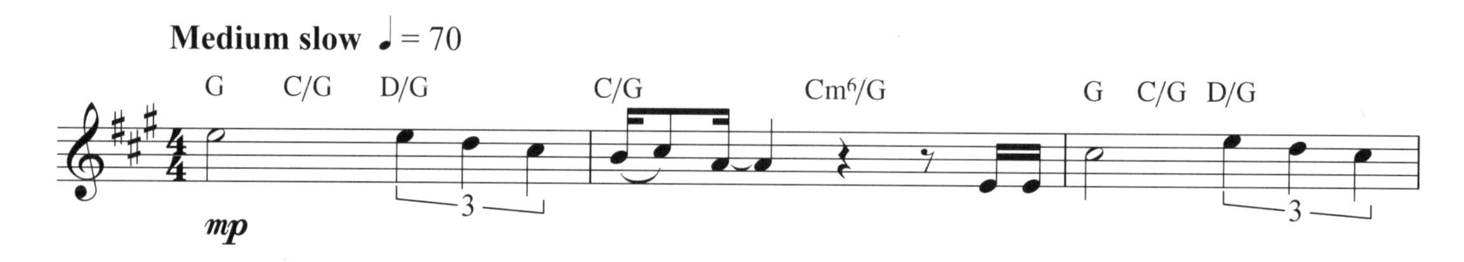

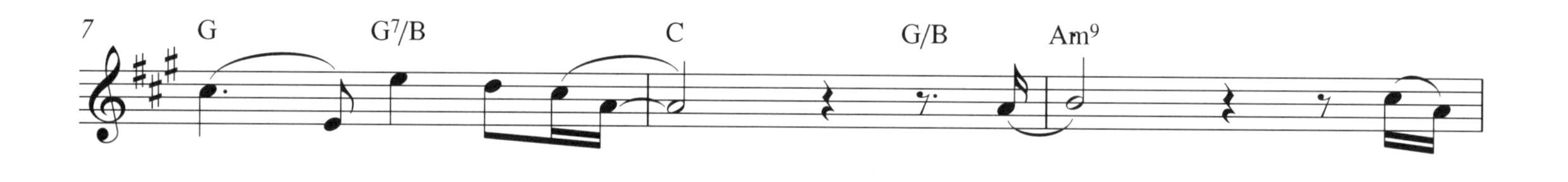

© Copyright 1982 Ensign Music Corporation/Famous Music LLC, USA.
Sony/ATV Harmony (UK) Limited.
All Rights Reserved. International Copyright Secured.

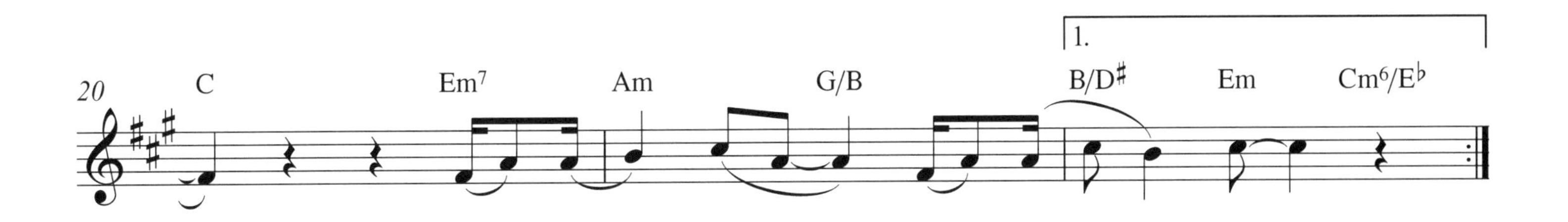

20
C
Em7
Am
G/B
1.
B/D♯
Em
Cm6/E♭

2.
23
A7/C♯
Dsus4
D/C
B♭
F/A
A♭
E♭/G

26
G♭
D♭/F
E♭
D♭/E♭
E♭
A♭
A♭/C

29
D♭
Fm7
B♭m
A♭/C
G♭
D♭/F
E♭

32
A♭
A♭/C
D♭
Fm7
B♭m
A♭/C

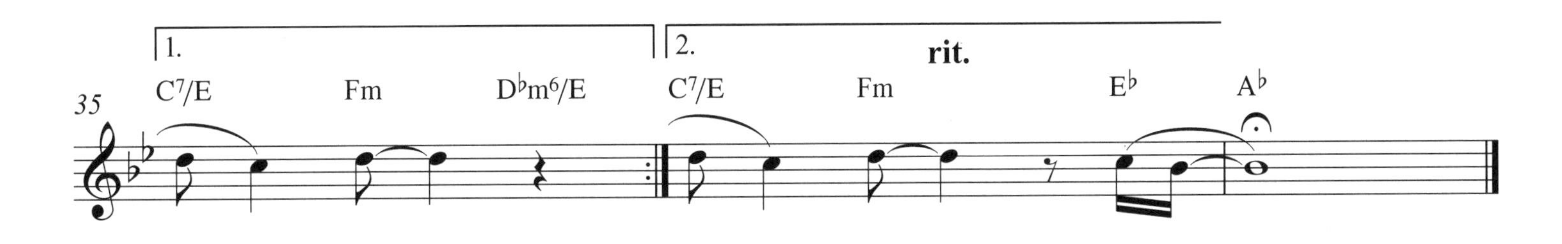

1.
2.
rit.
35
C7/E
Fm
D♭m6/E
C7/E
Fm
E♭
A♭

Voulez-Vous
(from 'Mamma Mia!')

Words & Music by Benny Andersson & Björn Ulvaeus

Bright disco feel ♩ = 126

© Copyright 1979 Union Songs AB, Sweden. Bocu Music Limited for Great Britain and the Republic of Ireland.
All rights in Germany administered by Universal Music Publ. GmbH.
All Rights Reserved. International Copyright Secured.

A Whole New World
(from 'Aladdin')

Words by Tim Rice & Music by Alan Menken

© Copyright 1992 Walt Disney Music Company Incorporated & Wonderland Music Company Incorporated, USA.
All Rights Reserved. International Copyright Secured.

You Know My Name
(Theme from 'James Bond: Casino Royale')

Words & Music by David Arnold & Chris Cornell

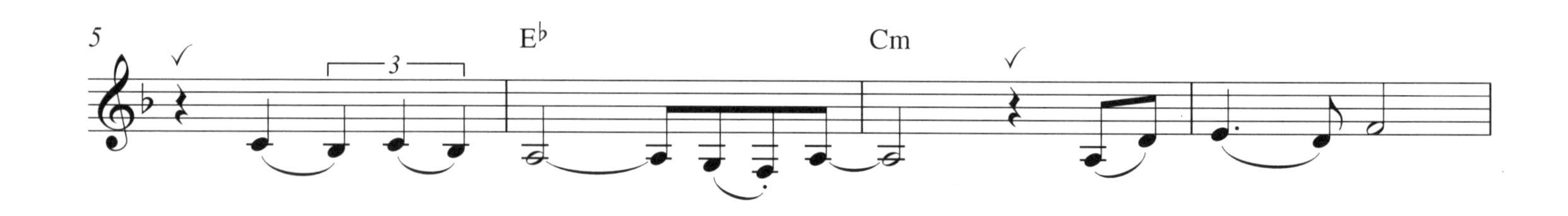

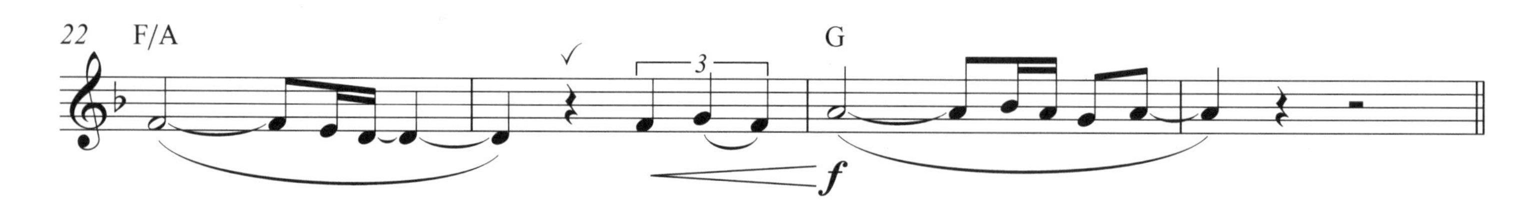

© Copyright 2006 EMI Music Publishing Limited (58.34%)/Sony/ATV Music Publishing (UK) Limited (30%)/Copyright Control (11.66%)
All Rights Reserved. International Copyright Secured.

26
Cm
A♭
F
3
f sempre
30
Cm
A♭
F
3
34
Cm
A♭
F
3
38
A♭
F
mf
1.
2.
42
Fm
Cm
A♭
F
3
47
A♭
F
mp dolce
51
A♭
F
3
mp
f

55
Cm
A♭
F
f sempre
59
Cm
A♭
F
63
Cm
A♭
F
67
A♭
F
mf
71
Fm
Cm
A♭
f
mf
75
F
Cm
A♭
f
mf
79
F
Cm
f
82
A♭
F
Cm

1 2 3 4 5 6 7 8 9